Front and back cover:
Variety of vegetables
Slide/Okapia/Reinhard

Pages 2/3:
Beans
Slide/Okapia/Reinhard

Pages 7 and 11:
Pumpkins

This edition published in 2002 by
CHARTWELL BOOKS, INC.
A division of Book Sales, Inc
114 Northfield Avenue
Edison, New Jersey 08837

© Molière 2002, Paris
ISBN: 0-7858-1542-2
Printed and bound in Italy
by Grafiche Zanini - Bologna

Photo credits:

Slide/Okapia: 1, 2/3, 11, 23, 25, 26/27, 31, 33, 35, 37, 39, 41, 42/43, 47, 49, 53, 55, 56/57, 61, 62/63, 64/65, 67, 68 /69, 71, 74/75, 81, 82/83, 85, 87, 89, 94/95, 99, 100/101, 102,103, 105, 109, 113, 115, 119, 129.
Slide: 45, 93, 117, 120.
Slide/Azambre: 29.
Slide/Binder: 96, 106/107.
Slide/Petri: 8.
Slide/Pontamier: 51.
Slide/Rosenthal: 78/79, 111.
Slide/Evans: 133.
Slide/Lemoine: 59, 73, 76/77, 91
Private collection, D.R.: 4, 7, 13, 15, 16, 17, 18, 19, 121, 122/123, 124/125, 126/127, 128, 133.

Text: E. Lemoine
Collaboration: F. B.S. B.

VEGETABLES
Then and Now

Elizabeth Lemoine

Foreword
Françoise Izrael

CHARTWELL
BOOKS, INC.

VEGETABLES
Then and Now

Elizabeth Lemoine

Foreword
Françoise Izrael

FOREWORD

Who would have said, at the end of the 40s, that in the 21st century, swedes and Jerusalem artichokes would be vegetables of choice? Or that gourds, pumpkins, chicories, colocynths, winter squash, turnips, and summer squash, which colored with their old-fashioned charm the kitchen gardens of our grandmothers, and were the basic ingredients of those soups we hated when we were younger, would become part of the most sophisticated cuisines and health practices? Or that we would be proud of growing tomatoes, peppers, fennel, cucumbers and radishes on our balconies and in our gardens?

Vegetables are lively plants which are not only subject to the cycles of nature, the sun, the moon, rain and frost, but also to people's whims. Formerly, when they did not accompany meat or fish, they were looked upon with a certain pity, as if they were orphans.

Today, vegetables have acquired their own autonomy, and, even when they are not part of a vegetarian diet, may be a meal by themselves. We keep finding in them new nourishing qualities and unsuspected medicinal properties and, at the same time, we rediscover to our great joy long forgotten vegetables the unusual flavors of which give free rein to our creativity. Let us hope that memory and imagination do combine to ensure that vegetables, the healthiest of foods for our bodies, are more and more present in our daily life.

Françoise IZRAEL

CONTENTS

A BRIEF HISTORY OF VEGETABLES

Who would have thought that at the beginning of the 21ˢᵗ century **beets** and **Jerusalem artichokes**, symbols of the deprivation that followed World War II, would become the preferred speciality served on silver plates in gastronomic temples? Or, that **aubergines** would be sold at prices comparable to those of caviar? These vegetables, which were once deemed the "meals of the poor" or as light and easily digestible dishes suitable only for those in convalescence, are popular today not only as the objects of detailed research, but as integral elements of vegetarian dishes present in the menus of some of the greatest restaurants.

The Romans, 2,000 years ago, were already familiar with the numerous properties of various vegetables, but they were not the first. In the words of *Pliny the Elder: "It would be impossible to enumerate the qualities of cabbage. Chrysippus already dedicated to it an entire volume divided into chapters each one dealing with a specific body part. Diocles also has written about it; even Pythagoras and Cato have praised this plant. A closer look at Cato's writings reveals the kind of medicine the Roman people have used for nearly 600 years. The early Greek authors distinguished three species: crinkled cabbage, which they named Selinas because its leaves resemble those of celery. This cabbage is good for the stomach and relaxes the abdomen. Smooth cabbage with large leaves which grow on a true stem [...] with no important medical properties. Cabbage, actually known as Crambe, with small, simple, very serrated leaves. It is very bitter, but very effective. Cato prefers the crinkled cabbage the most followed by the smooth cabbage with its large leaves and magnificent stem. He believes it is useful to treat headaches, flashing light sensations in the eye, blurred vision, stomach and diaphragm problems. It should be applied raw, mixed with vinegar, honey, coriander, rue, or mint [...]. To treat gout and joint illnesses it is mixed with rue, coriander, some salt and barley flour and applied in a compress. Use the decoction water, which is a marvellous aid for nerves and joints, in a compress. To heal old and fresh wounds, and to heal cartilage inflammations that cannot be cured by any other means, he recommends using the hot water in a compress and applying crushed cabbage twice a day."* The Roman naturalist observes the habits of his Roman predecessors with a certain condescension. Was he aware of the habits of the peoples of the Old Testament which, in fact, are surprisingly current today? *"(They) brought beds, and basins, and earthen vessels, and wheat, and barley, and flour, and parched corn, and beans, and lentils, and parched pulse, and honey, and butter, and sheep, and cheese of kine, for David, and for the people that were with him."* (Samuel II, 17 27:29). Despite the fact that none of the foods named have become obsolete, eating habits have evolved and vegetables have gone through waves of acceptance and rejection alike.

Lentils, which are mentioned very early in the book of Samuel, are an excellent example of the evolution and perpetuity of a vegetable. Before we begin, it is worth pointing out that we use the term "vegetable" in a very general sense, meaning: a food which is used as a side dish to compliment savory as well as sweet-and-savory dishes. **Lentils**, which are valued today because of their high iron content, are one of the oldest vegetables in the world. They can be traced as far back as the Neolithic Period. They have also been found in the Pharaohs' graves. The Romans allowed lentils to germinate before cooking them to intensify their sweetness and to prepare sweet and savory dishes. Later **lentils** were to experience a period of rejection. In the 19ᵗʰ century, for example, they were considered as meager refectory food.

The **pea** is also a very ancient vegetable with an interesting genetic history. During construction work on the Place du Carrousel in Paris, remains of **peas** dating from the Bronze Age were found. In the same way,

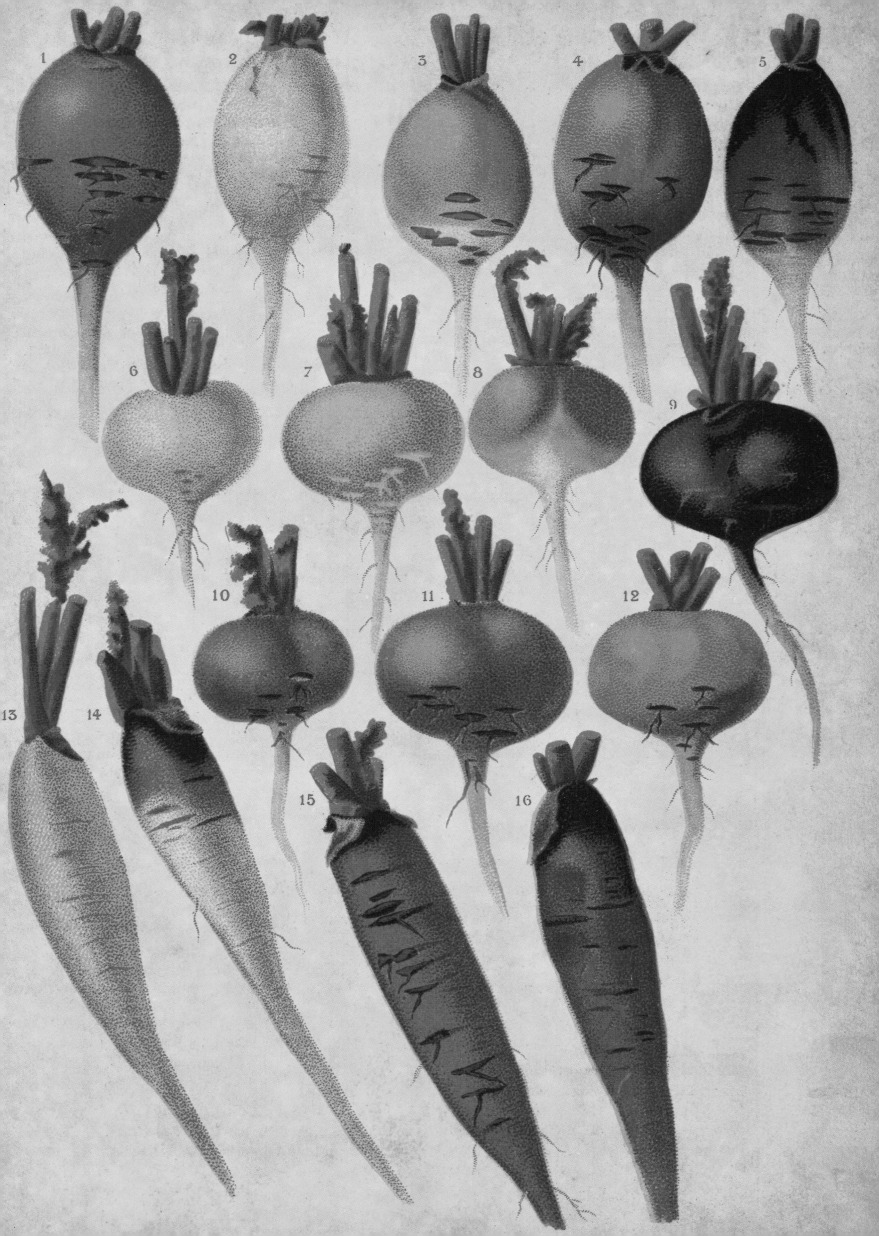

remains were also found in ancient Troy. It seems that a large, dry and coarse **pea** variety has survived from then to this day.

In the Middle Ages, this **pea** variety was so wide spread that it was the base ingredient in a stew served as part of the daily alms at monastery gates. In the Renaissance a completely different **pea** made its appearance with the **Medicis** in France. The small, delicate and sweet vegetable was well liked by **Louis XIV** and soon it became a favorite of the court. **La Quintinie**, who supervised the marvellous kitchen gardens of the king in Versailles, acclimatized it, leaving the plant unchanged. It was not until the next century that the Dutch developed its cultivation further. Today the **pea** is a widespread vegetable which has never fallen into oblivion and has not yet been completely rejected. **Peas**, fresh and tinned, are an important element in every day cooking; however, in gourmet cooking their popularity has declined.

Beans, which at the beginning of the 20th century were considered equivalent to **peas**, come from afar and have followed a very different path. In the Americas, the indigenous peoples cultivated the plant for its seeds, which, once ripe and dry, were a food that was easy to store. In the 16th century, **beans** were introduced to Europe where many different varieties were developed. Originally it was known as a dried vegetable with a high calorie content occasionally causing flatulence. Today, on the contrary, it has evolved to become a vegetable whose green, tender seedpods are consumed because they are rich in vitamins and low in calories. Fresh, they have become very stylish.

Lettuce and **corn salad** were already known in the late Middle Ages. **Lettuce** arrived in Avignon, France, with the popes in the 14th century. In the 16th century the first **cabbage lettuce** appeared and the vinaigrette was developed. **La Quintinie** cultivated **lettuces** in the royal garden because **Louis XIV** had a particular liking for them. **Corn salad** grew for a long time in the wild, and farmers collected it after mowing the meadows or weeding the vineyards. The French poet **Ronsard** praised its delicacy. In the 17th century attempts were made to breed varieties with bigger leaves without success, so it continued to be a wild plant. Some years later it became almost an industrialized product cultivated in a large way because of its popularity in Europe.

Tomatoes are a vegetable which is sometimes eaten raw and other times cooked. They are a good example of how species evolve. The Incas of the Peruvian Andes and the Aztecs of Mexico cultivated a small, yellow and bitter **tomato**. The Spanish conquistadors brought it to Europe where attempts were made to develop a breed that would better agree with the European taste. Nevertheless, the plant was regarded with suspicion as a food due to the fact that it is a close relative of poisonous plants such as mandragora, belladonna and deadly nightshade which were used in sorcery and witchcraft. Botanists would give it the name of *Lycopersicum cerasifome* (wolf peach). In the course of the following centuries, gardeners undertook different experiments, some of them with interesting results. In the 19th century, for example, **tomatoes** were grafted onto **potato** plants to harvest both fruit and tubers from a single plant; no one knows if the fruit were tasty, but the experiment was never repeated. The Italians seem to have been the first ones to adopt it as a fruit some time during the Renaissance. Soon its cultivation and consumption spread throughout Europe, and in the 19th century the plant crossed the Atlantic, back to its place of origin in the New World.

The **Chinese artichoke** is an example of a different evolutionary process. In Asia, its place of origin, it was not regarded as an edible plant until the 12th century. It was acclimatized to France, in 1882, by **Pailleux** and **Bois** in Crosne. It became a commercial product by chance: the farmers of the Somme in France, who competed in bulb cultivation with the Dutch, experienced a weather crisis and were forced to find an alternative crop which would prosper on their sandy soil. They went in search of a forgotten taste and, finally, came upon the **Chinese artichoke** which they cultivated successfully. After many years, this vegetable has slowly made its reappearance in the marketplace. Even though it is not very widespread, due to its taste, originality and quality, it has managed to capture the attention of those amateurs who prefer fine vegetables.

Broad beans belong to one of the oldest, most easily preserved food groups: cereals. It is believed that the **beans** were already being consumed in the 9th century BC. They are mentioned several times in the Old Testament: they were prepared with oil during normal times, but were treated like flour to make bread in times of need. Excavations in Gaul, France, show traces of **broad beans** dating from the Bronze Age. In the Middle Ages, they were a staple food; however, in the Renaissance, with the arrival of **green beans**, they

became less popular in Europe. In North Africa and in the Middle East they are still highly appreciated.

Wheat is not only one of the most popular cereals, it is also one of the most symbolic foods there is: a **wheat** field is almost sacred, reminding us of **Demeter**, Greek goddess of agriculture, Mother Earth, seed and fertility. At the same time, **wheat** fields have been the background of many conflicts. It is believed that **wheat** comes from a cereal originally found in Abyssinia which only had one large, hard grain. Accidentally, this grain crossbred with an unknown cereal producing an ear with multiple grains which, over the years, has been improved through selection. There are several very ancient and primitive varieties of **wheat**, and it is believed that all together there are at least 12,000 different **wheat** types. Crossbreeding must have taken place very early on; 8,000 years ago, starch **wheat** was already being cultivated in Kurdistan. In the 5th century BC, it was found in Iraq, Asia Minor and around the Mediterranean. It is frequently mentioned in the Bible: it was considered an excellent source of courage and strength. Cultivation areas for **wheat** were important to the Egyptians, the Greeks and especially the Romans who rewarded their veteran troops with "villa," properties surrounded by **wheat** fields. In the valleys of the Danube and the Rhine, a variety of wheat with stronger coated grains appeared.

The adaptability of **wheat** enables it to be grown in almost any country in the world, except tropical regions where there is not enough rainfall. In India a variety that is resistant to the tropical sun has been developed. Today, it is one of the crops with highest yields due to its resistance to disease and hardiness to cold. The most important **wheat** exporting countries are the United States, Canada, Argentina, the Ukraine, France and Australia.

Another very ancient cereal plant is **barley** which has been traced all the way back to prehistoric times. Even though this cereal was already cultivated, like **wheat** and **rye**, in ancient Egypt, bakers preferred to use **wheat**. The Greeks used unfermented **barley** to prepare a coarse bread known as *maza*, which had the shape of a big biscuit and was cooked on hot stones. It was given to slaves and disdained by wealthy people. Incidentally, it was **barley** bread that **Jesus-Christ** used in the feeding of the multitude to still the hunger of the crowd after the death of **John the Baptist**.

Millet is also a very ancient grain. Excavations prove that it was known 5,000 years before our time in China, as well as in Mesopotamia, later in Egypt, Greece and Western Europe. In France, on the banks of lake Annecey, traces have been found which date back to the Bronze Age. Today, this grain is a staple food for millions of people in Asia and Siberia. During the big

Carrot

The carrot is one of the oldest cultivated vegetables. It comes from a wild variety found in Asia. It is mentioned in the Bible and in the Koran as a valuable food source. The first traces of its culture go back at least six millennia before our time. Pliny the Elder named it the "Gallic root" (Pastinaca gallica). It appeared on the Iberian peninsula following the invasion of the Moors. It was also found in the kitchen gardens of Charlemagne.

Originally the roots were white, but for some unknown reason, in Afghanistan they spontaneously turned orange. Latter, a similar orange root was discovered in Holland which then spread to England. Since the beginning of the 19th century many different carrot varieties have been developed.

Potato

Potato has its origins in the Andean mountains where this tuber has long been known under the name of papa. Images portraying potatoes on early ceramics dating from before Inca times have been found. The Spanish conquistadors brought the potato to Spain where it was first cultivated as in its place of origin. In 1534 the potato arrived in France, later spread to Italy and soon to the rest of Europe where it was used as livestock feed. At that time, the tubers were still small, bitter and indigestible. The military pharmacist Antoine-Auguste Parmentier, while living under captivity in Germany, was forced to survive on potatoes. He discovered that potatoes were not harmful and that they had a high nutritional value. When he was freed and under the patronage of Louis XVI, he began to cultivate potatoes, improving their taste.

famine after the October Revolution in Russia, it was for many the only source of nourishment. Today, in the western world, it has fallen into oblivion and it is only processed in bread mixtures. Germinated **millet** grains are used in the vegetarian kitchen. However, the grains are mostly used as bird food.

When **Christopher Columbus** arrived in the Americas and saw **corn** for the first time, he thought it was **rice**, the plant so many other navigators had described before. On the 5th of November 1492 he wrote in a letter that these ears had a good taste and that all the inhabitants of the region survived on this plant. In 1519 when **Cortés** arrived in Mexico, he also noted that the cultivation of this plant was particularly simple requiring only superficial fertilizing of the ground. Both navigators were impressed with the density of the crop and its extraordinary yield. They also pointed out that the native people never seemed to suffer from hunger. At the time, food in Europe was scarce. **Columbus** brought **corn** seeds to Spain to be planted. Soon **corn** cultivation had spread throughout the Mediterranean region; it was used

in Italy to make polenta and in Turkey to prepare a national dish. The flour obtained from this new cereal was also mixed with other flours to make bread, but due to its yellow color it was never very successful in Europe.

Corn, which was also known as Turkish, Indian or Spanish wheat was cultivated in France during the 17th century where it was used for both human and animal consumption. Today **corn** is one of the most widely distributed food plants ranking third in world cereal production. The main producing countries are the United States, China, Russia and France.

Rice is one of the oldest of foods. Its development and its longevity are striking. There are more similarities than differences between rough **rice**, which for many years has been the basic ingredient of the Asian diet, and more refined and elaborate **rice** varieties sold in gourmet stores. The origins of **rice** cultivation can be traced back to China in about 2,800 BC and to India in about 2,300 BC. It was also known by the peoples of Egypt, Persia and Macedonia, but it only arrived in Europe during the 8th century with the invasion of the Moors in Spain. From there it spread onto the Camargue and the Po Valley where it is still cultivated today. **Rice** arrived in North America in 1615, when an English ship caught in a storm took refuge in Charleston on the coast of South Carolina. In appreciation for the way he and his crew had been treated, captain **James Thurber** gave **rice** plants to the distinguished people of the city. These plants are the ancestors of the **rice** plants we find today in South Carolina.

The **soy bean**, formerly known as *Dilochos soja*, is a herbaceous plant native to the warm regions of the earth. It is grown predominantly in China, but it is also cultivated in Japan and other Asian countries. The plant was not introduced to Europe until the 18th century as a botanical curiosity. By the end of 19th century it gained

considerable importance not only in the food industry, but also in the medical field. It was introduced to France in 1740 by missionaries who brought it from China. **Soy milk** was produced for the first time in Paris in 1910. In the United States **soy beans** have been cultivated since 1880 quite successfully.

Earth almond now brings us close to the valley of the white Nile and Sudan where it grows in the wild. Tubers of this plant have been found in the tombs of the Pharaohs. **Theophrastus** describes it as an edible plant which grows near water, and he even offers us an interesting recipe: tubers should be cooked in boiling beer. Today, this oil plant is cultivated in Spain, Italy, Hungary, the United States and Russia.

Sorghum takes us to the tropics. In Egypt, during the times of the Pharaohs, **sorghum** was not used for human consumption but was given to livestock instead. It was introduced to France under the name of "broomcorn," and was used for centuries to manufacture brooms and brushes. The *Sorghum saccharatum* variety comes from China where it is known as **kaoliang**. It is rich in sugar; therefore, it is used to produce sugar and alcohol. Because of the different properties possessed by each variety, the one providing fodder and the other sugar, producers decided to crossbreed them. The result was **sorghum bicolor**, a grain cereal of great importance throughout the world. It is a staple food in India, Africa and China. Researchers have also produced a fodder variety called "Haygrazer," which is used to promote the fast growth of pasture land.

We end our journey with a very unusual edible plant: **nettle**. This plant, whose properties were ignored for a very long time, has followed man since the Neolithic period. In the Bible, this peculiar companion is the symbol of laziness, idleness, desolation and ruin; fields which were badly maintained were depicted as being covered with **nettles**. It was regarded as harmful to agriculture and injurious to man when touched, causing a burning sensation and leaving scars on the skin. In the Middle Ages, it was used to treat a number of different ailments. In France, for example, a **nettle** bouquet was given to the bridegroom so he would rub it on his bride, if on their honeymoon she did not show enough passion. A beating with **nettles** was also used as a punishment for naughty children. Soon, in the northern part of Europe, especially in Sweden, the plant was exploited in a different way. It was cultivated and became a fodder plant resistant to drought with the advantage that it developed quickly. Since then, in the north, the young seedlings are used as a potherb. **Nettle** leaves are used to feed bovine animals, pigs, ducks and geese, and the seeds to feed birds. The fibers found in its stem are used to produce fabric and paper. For a long time it was used only in certain regions, while it was ignored throughout most of the world. Today, thanks to advances in technology, we are beginning to discover the medicinal and nutritional properties of this prehistoric and wild plant which has never been well liked.

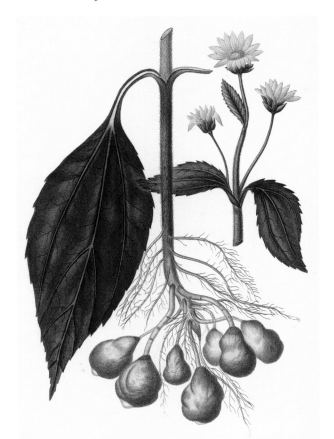

After the great famine of 1770, potatoes began to be more popular and by 1785 they had become a staple food. In the mid-19th century, Irish potato crops were damaged by late blight fungus causing potato famines. As a result of this, many Irish people emigrated to the United States taking some potato plants along with them. This time the plants were attacked by an insect known as the Colorado beetle. This insect was transported in trading vessels back to Bordeaux from where it spread throughout Europe. Late blight disease was no longer a threat because it had been brought under control by using copper sulphate; however, there was nothing that could help fight the Colorado beetle. Many solutions were tried without success. Finally, the plants were bred to make them resistant against this insect. Today potatoes are a staple food in many countries.

Jerusalem Artichoke

Samuel de Champlain brought the tubers of this plant to Europe, after he discovered that the Indians used it as food. The plant, which comes from Canada, has experienced short waves of rejection. It was very popular during the war, but soon it was to disappear from the marketplace. Today the tubers are considered a luxurious extravagance.

VEGETABLES AS REMEDIES

CARDIO-VASCULAR SYSTEM

ANAEMIA - SORGHUM *seeds, germinated* WHEAT *kernels,* COW PARSNIP *vegetable leaves,* MILLET *seeds and porridge, whole and ground* DRY BEANS.

ARTERIOSCLEROSIS - *germinated* WHEAT *kernels,* SOY BEAN *seeds and flour.*

BLOOD CLOTS - *infusions of* COW PARSNIP *leaves and seedlings,* CARDOON *stems,* ARTICHOKE *heart and leaves,* JERUSALEM ARTICHOKE *tubers,* GREEN BEANS, *raw or grated* RADISH *roots,* SCORZONERA *root and juice, infusions of* LADY'S MANTEL, *decoction of* CHICORY *roots.*

BRUISES - COW PARSNIP *leaves in a compress or in infusions.*

CHOLESTEROL - SORGHUM *seeds, germinated* WHEAT *kernels, germinated* CORN KERNELS, OAT *grains, and* SOY BEAN *seeds and flour.*

CIRCULATION - SNAKE GOURD *pulp,* COW PARSNIP *infusions.*

HAEMOPHILIA - *infusions with* CORN SPIKLETS.

HAEMORRHOIDS - *wild* CUCUMBER *balm.*

HEART - *germinated* WHEAT *kernels,* ONION, *germinated* BARLEY *kernels, green* BEANS, AUBERGINE *pulp, germinated* SORGHUM *roasted like* COFFEE *in infusions.*

HIGH BLOOD PRESSURE - *fresh* ORACH *leaves,* EARTH ALMOND *oil,* MILLET *seeds and flour, raw* SPINACH.

LOW BLOOD PRESSURE - *infusions of* GERMINATED BARLEY.

MEMORY - BEETROOT, SOY BEAN *seeds,* PEAS.

MENOPAUSE - *infusions with* LADY'S MANTEL, FRESH CARROT *roots,* SOY BEAN *grains seeds, germ and flour,* ALFALFA *leaves in salads, decoction of* RHUBARB *roots.*

UREA - SALSIFY *roots to promote perspiration, infusions with* BAOBAB *leaves.*

DIGESTIVE SYSTEM

ABDOMINAL COLIC - *poultice with* POTATOES, *decoction of* CARROT *seeds, cooking water of* RICE, *cooked* CUCUMBER *and* SQUASH.

AEROPHAGIA - FENNEL, *seeds and cooking water.*

APPETITE STIMULANTS - *fresh* SPINACH *leaves in salads and in juice, fresh* CELERY *stems and roots raw and grated, raw* PEPPER, ENDIVE *salad, fresh* WATERCRESS, TOMATOES.

APPETITE SUPPRESSANTS - *ground* CORN *salad, cooked* TANIA *pulp, flour made of from* TANIA *tubers.*

COLITIS - *infusions with* LADY'S MANTEL *leaves, infusions with* CARROT *seeds, raw* ONIONS, *raw* RADISH, *and whole* RICE.

CONSTIPATION - *cooked* SPINACH *leaves, whole* WHEAT, AUBERGINE, CHINESE ARTICHOKE, CHARD, ONION, LEEK, POTATO, TOMATO, JERUSALEM ARTICHOKE, MALABAR SPINACH, SEA KALE, CARDOON, CHICORY *salad,* PUMPKIN *soup.*

DIARRHOEA - *infusions with* NETTLE, LADY'S MANTEL *in warm wine,* BAOBAB, CABBAGE, PUMPKIN PULP, MILLET, BARLEY, RICE, CHINESE CABBAGE, ORACH *and* RHUBARB.

DIGESTION - *decoction of* COW PARSNIP *roots, infusions with* PARSLEY *seeds,* LEEK, SWEET PEAS, LETTUCE, FENNEL, MANIOC, GOURD.

INDIGESTION - *infusions with* FENNEL *seeds, cooked* ASPARAGUS, GOOSEFOOT *salad,* RHUBARB *wine.*

STOMACH - *infusions with* RHUBARB *roots,* CARROT, BARLEY, POTATO, PUMPKIN, GOURD, FENNEL, LENTILS.

VOMITING - HONEY *with* BELL PEPPER *powder.*

MUSCULO-SKELETAL SYSTEM

ARTHRITIS - NETTLE, BAMBOO *seedling,* RADISH, LEEK *stock,* CORN *salad.*

GOUT - CABBAGE, CORN, SALSIFY, SCORZONERA, TOMATO, *decoction of* ARTICHOKE *leaves.*

LUMBAGO - *poultice with boiled* CABBAGE *leaves.*

OSTEOPOROSIS - WHEAT, SOY BEANS, *raw* SPINACH *leaves,* ALFALFA SPROUTS, RADISH, BEETROOT, BAMBOO *seedlings.*

RHEUMATIC PAIN - SORGHUM, PUMPKIN, GREEN BEANS *and* CELERY *juice, decoction of* SALSIFY *roots,* BURDOCK *leaves, poultice with cooked* BURDOCK LEAVES, *raw and crushed* CABBAGE *leaves, chopped raw* ONIONS.

RICKETS - *germinated* WHEAT, SPINACH, PARSLEY, CUCUMBER, QUINOA, MILLET, SOY BEANS.

SCIATICA - *poultice with raw* CABBAGE *leaves, massage with fresh* NETTLE.

RESPIRATORY SYSTEM

ASTHMA - COW PARSNIP *seeds in liqueur, infusions with* CORN *salad roots,* RADISH *syrup, infusions with* SCORZONERA *roots.*

BRONCHITIS - TURNIP ROOTED CHERVIL: *infusions with the whole plant, decoctions of* LEEK, CARROTS, SCORZONERA, ONION, BARLEY, CELERIAC, CABBAGE, BLACK RADISH *syrup, poultice of* BARLEY *flour.*

COUGH - *infusions with* ONION, *decoctions of* CARROT *and* LETTUCE, LEEK *and* BLACK RADISH *syrup, decoctions of* SCORZONERA *roots.*

DRY MOUTH - TURNIP ROOTED CHERVIL *roots crushed or in a decoction.*

INFLUENZA - *decoctions of* CARLINE THISTLE ROOTS, *with* ASPARAGUS *and with* MILLET, COW PARSNIP, *fresh ground* RADISH ROOT.

LARYNGITIS - LEEK *juice, decoction of* LADY'S MANTEL *leaves used as gargle.*

TONSILLITIS - *infusions of* LADY'S MANTEL, *infusions with* RAMPION *roots, gargles with* BARLEY SEEDS, CELERY *juice, cooked* LEEK *poultice.*

URINARY AND REPRODUCTIVE SYSTEMS

AMENORRHOEA - STINGING NETTLE *juice, decoction of* LADY'S MANTEL, *ground* CORN *salad root, infusions with germinated* BARLEY *seeds.*

IMPOTENCE - PARSLEY, OATS, *germinated* WHEAT, COW PARSNIP *ground and diluted in wine.*

INFERTILITY - OATS, WHEAT, ARTICHOKE, POTATO, LEEK.

IRREGULAR MENSTRUATION - *infusions with* CARROT *leaves and seeds, decoction of* COW PARSNIP *root, infusions with* LADY'S MANTEL, *fresh* PARSLEY *juice.*

LEUCORRHEA - *douche with decocted* PARSLEY *leaves, fresh* NETTLE *juice,* NETTLE *flower infusion.*

SEXUAL FATIGUE - CELERY, CELERIAC *and* FENNEL *as vegetables,* COW PARSNIP *infusion.*

NERVOUS SYSTEM

ANXIETY, NERVOUSNESS, SPASMS - WHEAT, SOY BEANS *in all its their forms,* TURNIP, GOURD, *decoctions of* LETTUCE.

CEREBRAL FUNCTION - BEETROOT *and* SOY BEAN *in all its forms.*

INSOMNIA - *fresh* LETTUCE *or decoction of the leaves, cooked* ASPARAGUS, PARSNIP.

MIGRAINE, NEURALGIA - *decoction of* CORN *and* LADY'S MANTEL.

MOUTH PROBLEMS

ABSCESSES - *fresh* GARDEN CRESS *and* WATERCRESS.

BLISTERS - *decoctions of* NETTLE.

CAVITIES - *chew* WHEAT *as a preventive measure.*

CHAPPED LIPS - *rub with a fresh slice of* CUCUMBER.

TOOTH PAIN - CORN *infusions.*

LIVER PROBLEMS

BILE DUCTS - ARTICHOKE, ASPARAGUS, AUBERGINE, BEETROOT, CARDOON, CARROT, CHERVIL, CHICORY, CABBAGE, GARDEN CRESS, CHINESE ARTICHOKE, GREEN BEANS, RADISH, SALSIFY, SCORZONERA, *decoctions of* CARLINE THISTLE *and* ARTICHOKE *leaves.*

GALL BLADDER - *decoction of* ARTICHOKE *leaves, fresh* RADISH *juice.*

GALLSTONES - CELERY *decoction,* CORN *and* BURDOCK.

JAUNDICE - *infusions with* CHERVIL, *decoctions of* CHICORY.

HAIR AND NAIL PROBLEMS

ATHLETES FOOT - *drink the cooking water of* SCORZONERA.

HAIR GROWTH - BURDOCK *root ointment, decoctions of* BURDOCK *and* NETTLE *roots,* GARDEN CRESS *juice and fresh* NETTLE *leaves.*

HAIR LOSS - *eat raw* GARDEN CRESS *or drink its juice.*

PALE, GROOVED NAILS - *cooked* ONION *poultice,* WHITE LEAK *leaves cooked,* ONION *juice in a compress,* CABBAGE *leaves.*

SHINY BLOND HAIR - *decoctions of* RHUBARB *flowers.*

SHINY BRUNETTE HAIR - LEEK *juice.*

SPLIT, BRITTLE NAILS - *germinated* WHEAT, SOY BEAN, FRESH NETTLE *or* GARDEN CRESS *juice in a compress.*

SKIN PROBLEMS

ABSCESSES - *burdock root in a poultice, fresh* POTATO *pulp, fresh* LEEK *juice in a compress, ground* CARROT, *raw* CABBAGE *leaves, cooked* LENTILS, ONION, RHUBARB.

ACNE - *compress with* NETTLE *and* CABBAGE *juice, decoctions of* CARLINE THISTLE *and* LETTUCE *leaves,* PARSLEY, RADISH, TOMATO, CABBAGE *and* SPINACH *juice.*

BLOTCHY COMPLEXION - *decoction of* LETTUCE *leaves in a compress.*

CHAPPED SKIN - *raw* ONION *plaster.*

CHILBLAIN - *decoction of whole* CARROT *and* CELERY *leaves in a poultice.*

CONGESTED SKIN - *fresh* CUCUMBER *juice.*

ECZEMA - *fresh* BURDOCK *leaves in a poultice, fresh* CABBAGE *juice in a compress, decoction of* CARLINE THISTLE.

ERYTHEMA - *fresh* CUCUMBER *juice.*

GRAY SKIN, DULL COMPLEXION - *decoctions of* BURDOCK *root,* CARROT, CHICORY, SALSIFY, LEEK *juice, infusions with nettle leaves.*

HARSH, DIRTY SKIN - *to clean the skin, mix fresh* CARROT *juice,* CUCUMBER *and* GARDEN CRESS, *decoction of* SCORZONERA, CHERVIL *and* NETTLE *lotions.*

HIVES - NETTLE *decoction.*

IMPETIGO - *poultice with fresh* BURDOCK *leaves, compress with fresh* CABBAGE *juice.*

IRRITATION - *poultice with* RICE *flour, decoction of* CARLINE THISTLE *in a compress, germinated* WHEAT, CAULIFLOWER, *on blisters apply wild* CUCUMBER *balm.*

ITCHING - *decoction with* SWEET PEAS, *mask with* DRY BEAN *flour.*

PSORIASIS - *decoction of* NETTLE *used in a compress.*

RASHES - *decoction of* BEET, CORN *infusions*, PUMPKIN.
RED SPOTS - PARSLEY *juice*, ONION *paste with vinegar*.
SCABIES - *cream with cooked wild* CUCUMBER *roots*.
STRETCH MARKS - *decoction of* LADY'S MANTEL *used in a compress*.
SUN BURN - *sliced* POTATOES, ALFALFA SPROUTS
and ground RADISH *in a compress*, TOMATO *salad*.
ULCERS - ONION *vinegar, poultice with raw, crushed* CABBAGE *leaves*, CARROT, BURDOCK.
WARTS - RAMPION *leaves crushed into a plaster,*
compress with fresh ONION *juice*, SALSIFY.
WOUNDS, CUTANEOUS BLEEDING - *plasters with* POTATO *pulp, wild* CUCUMBER,
compress with crushed LADY'S MANTEL *leaves*, BURDOCK, CABBAGE *juice*.

KIDNEY AND GLANDULAR PROBLEMS

ALBUMINURIA - *in the evening,* ONIONS, *decoction of* CELERY *roots, dried* BEANS, CORN,
infusion with LEEK *seeds*.
CYSTITIS - *infusions with* STINGING NETTLE, BAOBAB,
CORN, FRESH TOMATOES.
DIURESIS - *decoction of* ASPARAGUS, LEEK *seed wine,* PARSNIP *or* LEEK *porridge*.
ENURESIS - *in the evening,* WHEAT *and* NETTLE *cookies*.
KIDNEY STONES - CHARD *decoctions,* CORN.
NEPHRITIC COLIC - *warm plasters with* CABBAGE *leaves*.
NEPHRITIS - *infusions with wild* CUCUMBER *pulp raw or cooked*.
RENAL INSUFFICIENCY - LEEK, SPINACH, ASPARAGUS, CARDOONS, CELERIAC *and* CELERY.

EYE PROBLEMS

CONJUNCTIVITIS - *compress and rinse with a decoction of* LADY'S MANTEL *leaves*.
NIGHT BLINDNESS - *decoction of* CARROT *root*.
OPHTHALMIA - CHERVIL *or* PARSLEY *juice applied as eye drops*.
SWOLLEN EYELIDS - *thin, raw* POTATO *slices*.

OTHER AILMENTS

ACOUPHENE - ONION *juice in on cottonwood balls in the ear, roasted*
MILLET *seeds with coarse salt on gauze in the ear*.
APHONIA - LEEK JUICE.
BREAST FEEDING DIFFICULTY - LENTILS, JERUSALEM ARTICHOKE,
FENNEL, *infusions with germinated* BARLEY.
BURNS - *poultice of cooked* SPINACH *leaves*, ORACH, CARROT,
crinkled CABBAGE *leaves, fresh* PUMPKIN *pulp,*
cooked BEAN *puree, raw* ONION *juice, fresh* POTATO *leaves*.
OEDEMA - NETTLE *decoctions*, CORN, PARSLEY *infusions, raw wine* ONION, LEEK *seed wine*.
EXHAUSTION, FATIGUE, CONVALESCENCE - *raw* ONIONS, CARROT, CABBAGE, TOMATO, BELL
PEPPERS, GARDEN CRESS, *as a vegetable cooked* LENTILS, CELERY, BEETROOT, SALSIFY, OATS,
SOY BEAN LEEK, MILLET, PEAS.
FEVER - *infusions with* BAOBAB *leaves*, CARLINE THISTLE.
IMPOTENCE - *eat* OATS, *germinated* WHEAT,
drink the wine of COW PARSNIP *root and leaves*.
MICROBIAL AND VIRAL AILMENTS - BEETROOT, CABBAGE *in all its forms,*
fresh BELL PEPPERS, GARDEN CRESS *salad*.
OBESITY - AUBERGINE, CELERY, CORN SALAD, PARSNIP, LEEK, TURNIP, CHINESE ARTICHOKE,
OKRA, CUCUMBER, *drink* ARTICHOKE *infusions*.
PHYSICAL AND INTELLECTUAL EXHAUSTION - BEETROOT *juice, eat* GREEN PEAS.
SCURVY - *fresh* CABBAGE *juice*, GARDEN CRESS, ALFALFA SPROUTS, RADISH.
WEANING - *poultice wit fresh* PARSLEY *and* CHERVIL *leaves*.

GLOSSARY OF MEDICAL PROPERTIES

ANTISCORBUTIC: *fights scurvy.*
ANTISEPTIC : *stops infections and destroys microbes.*
ANTISPASMODIC: *see calmant.*
APPETITIVE : *stimulates the appetite.*
ASTRINGENT : *diminishes the secretions*
of glands and mucous membranes.
BALSAMIC : *stimulates the digestive and respiratory tracts.*
CARMINATIVE : *favors the elimination of gas and calms stomach pains.*
DIURETIC : *increases the excretion of urine.*
EMETIC : *favors vomiting.*
EMMENAGOGUE : *provokes, facilitates menstrual flow.*
EMOLLIENT : *soothes and calms inflammation of tissues.*
EXPECTORANT : *eases the bringing up of phlegm*
and mucus from the respiratory tract.

FEBRIFUGE : *lowers fevers.*
GALACTOGENIC: *favoring milk production.*
HEMOSTATIC : *stops bleeding.*
LAXATIVE : *loosens the bowels and relieves constipation.*
PURGATIVE : *cleans the intestines.*
PURIFIER : *cleanses the blood from impurities.*
SEDATIVE : *soothes and calms the nervous system.*
STIMULANT : *augments energy*
of the vital functions.
STOMACHIC : *excites the appetite.*
SUDORIFIC : *favors perspiration.*
TONIC : *strengthens the organism.*
VULNERARY : *externally, heals wounds;*
internally, combats physical weakness.

GLOSSARY OF TECHNICAL TERMS

ALTERNATE : *leaves arranged at different levels on the stem;*
one leaf to a node.
BERRY : *fleshy fruit with pips.*
BIPINNATE : *leaves formed of pinnate divisions, themselves formed*
of pinnate leaflets.
BRACT : *leaf at the base of a flower, usually much reduced in*
size.
CARPEL : *female organ of the flower.*
CORDATE : *heart shaped.*
COUMARIN : *a greasy, fragrant substance.*
CUPULE : *a series of closed bracts that form a cup beneath the*
fruit.
DECOCTION : *a preparation made by putting the plant in cold water*
and heating to a boil.
DIOECIOUS : *having male and female flowers on separate plants.*
EVEN-PINNATE : *compound leaf with an even number of leaflets.*
INFUSION : *an herbal tea prepared by pouring boiling water on*
the plant and allowing to stand for 5 to 10 minutes.
LEAFLET : *division of a compound leaf.*
MELLIFEROUS : *producing honey.*
MONOECIOUS : *a plant bearing both male and female flowers.*
MONOSPERMOUS : *having only one seed.*

ODD-PINNATE : *leaf having an uneven number of leaflets*
with a terminal leaflet.
PEDUNCLE : *small ramification of the stem ending in a flower.*
PERENNIAL : *said of a plant that survives several years and that*
flowers every year, the aerial parts disappearing each
winter.
PINNATE : *feather-like; leaflets arranged along a central leaf*
axis.
PUBESCENCE : *the soft down that covers the surface of many plants.*
RHIZOME : *perennial subterranean stem.*
ROSETTE : *a radiating leaf cluster at or near the base of the plant.*
SELF-POLLINATION : *pollen is transferred from the anthers to the stigmas in the*
same flower.
SESSILE : *attached directly to the stem without a peduncle.*
SILIQUE : *dehiscent fruit opening in four parts.*
SPADIX : *inflorescence surrounded by a large bract.*
STALK : *also petiole, the main stem or axis of a plant.*
STEM : *the main upward-growing axis of a plant.*
STOLON : *creeping aerial or subterranean stem by which the*
plant propagates.
VERTICILATE : *an almost circular arrangement of leaves or flowers at the*
same level of the stem.

THESE NATURAL REMEDIES ARE NOT BY ANY MEANS INTENDED
TO REPLACE MEDICINES PRESCRIBED BY A DOCTOR.

VEGETABLES FROM A TO Z

ABELMOSCHUS ESCULENTUS	**Okra**
Fruit vegetable	
Family: Malvaceae	
Origin: tropical Africa	
Height: 3 to 6.5 feet (1 to 2 m)	
Flowering: late spring	
Properties: digestive, laxative, stomachic	

ADANSONIA DIGITATA	**Baobab**
Leaf vegetable	
Family: Bombaceae	
Origin: African Savanna	
Height: 6.5 feet (2 m)	
Flowering: summer	
Properties: anti-diarrhoea, febrifuge, sedative	

Okra arrived in Egypt, where the Pharaohs began to successfully cultivate it, from Africa. Later, it spread to tropical and subtropical Asia and America where it is still grown today.

It is an herbaceous, annual plant with long, ramified, erect stems. Its alternate, very lobed leaves, which are smooth on top and hairy underneath, have a long petiole. Its splendid solitary flowers, measuring about 3 inches (8 cm) in diameter, appear on the ends of superior leaves. They are generally yellow, sometimes white or reddish, like those of the Syrian **okra**, with a violet-blue center. They render an edible fruit or pod, hairy at the base which is a capsule, measuring about 4 to 10 inches (10–25 cm) in length, that contains numerous oval, dark colored seeds. This fruit has a sweet, delicate flavor.

Okra is grown from seed at a minimum temperature of 59 °F (15 °C). Once the pods have been harvested, the seeds are sown on plain soil. Harvesting is done while the fruit is still tender and unripe, because ripe **okra** is very fibrous with several hard grains which are not pleasant to the palate. To preserve the fruit, it is dried in the sun and later pickled or frozen. **Okra** is rich in mucilage, vitamins, and mineral salts. Due to its high mucilage content, it is recommended for weight loss and stomach problems. Its roots are used in the manufacture of paper.

Its unique size and longevity make this tree the giant of the vegetable kingdom. It was named after the French botanist **Adanson** who spent time studying it in Senegal, the tree's place of origin. Even though it is a tree and not a plant, the **baobab**, due to its medicinal and nutritional properties, is considered to be a great vegetable and a very useful plant.

Although the tree spreads itself out, it does not have many branches. It has a short, deformed, stalky trunk that can reach 30 feet (9 m) in diameter. Its large digitally compound leaves, with long leaflets sprout on the young branches, fall during the dry season. The solitary terminal flowers hang from a long peduncle. They are formed by a calyx of five white petals with a long pistil and numerous stamens that bear fruit in the shape of oval-pointed capsules which can be almost 12 inches (30 cm) long and 6 inches (15 cm) wide. Their woody bark has a very thick green covering. This fruit, known to the native people of Senegal as "bread of the apes," is divided in several segments containing various kidney shaped seeds enclosed in a floury, fibrous sweet-and-sour pulp.

The **baobab** contains alkaloids, tannin, sugar, oil, vitamins and minerals. Its bark is used to extract an alkaloid which serves as an antidote for curare poison. Its leaves regulate breathing allowing the elimination of

Okra

This vegetable is used fresh in salads or cooked in ragouts. When cooked in salted water, with or without spices, this clear, viscose preparation is known in the Creole kitchen as Calalou. It can also be boiled like green beans, fried in a pan, baked in the oven or used as an ingredient for a gratin. When dried, okra must first be soaked. The powder obtained from drying and crushing the ripe vegetables is also used to thicken sauces. The grains can be roasted to obtain a drink similar to coffee. They also contain an oil used in certain drinks and perfumes.

toxins. An infusion of the leaves is used to alleviate diarrhoea, fever and urinary problems.

The leaves are prepared like any other green vegetable: fresh, in salads; cooked in baked pies, stews and gratins accompanying both meat and fish. *Lalo*, as it is known to the local people, is a nutritional supplement made by drying the leaves in the shade and crushing them to a powder.

AEGOPODIUM PODAGRARIA   **Goutweed**
Leaf vegetable
Family: *Umbelliferae*
Origin: *Europe and western Asia*
Height: *31 inches (80 cm)*
Flowering: *May to July*
Properties: *astringent, mineralizing, tonic*

Goutweed is a perennial plant renowned in antiquity for its medicinal properties. It thrives easily in a shady underground with rich humid soil. Its characteristic scent resembles that of the **carrot**. This wild vegetable is propagated through its strongly ramified rhizome which has alternate, feather-divided leaves that are sheathed at the base. Its leaflets are pointed, lanceolate and dentate. Its trunk is hairy, branched, hollow, angular and channelled. The flowers, white or pink, are usually arranged in conspicuous umbels. They bear an achene fruit that is ovoid and flat on the sides.

Goutweed is propagated through the new rhizome shoots which are planted in the shade in a humid, fertile soil that is rich in nitrogen; this plant is rarely propagated from seed. Seedlings which have not yet bloomed are harvested, as are the leaves during the entire growth period of the plant. **Goutweed** is rich in mineral salts. Its leaves contain carotene and are rich in vitamin C. Because of its medicinal properties, it is used in health spas and during convalescence for its invigorating and revitalizing effect on the body.

Goutweed
The leaves and young shoots can be used in salads, or cooked in stews. The leaves can also be cooked in oil with onions, garlic, a pinch of nutmeg, salt, potatoes, and whipped cream, and served as a side dish for meat, eggs or fish.

ALCHEMILLA XANTHOCHLORA   **Lady's mantel**
Leaf vegetable
Family: *Rosaceae*
Origin: *Europe, western Asia, North Africa and Canada*
Height: *about 12 inches (30 cm)*
Flowering: *May to September*
Properties: *anti-inflammatory, astringent, laxative, digestive, diuretic, emollient, emmenagogue, stomachic*

In former times, alchemists collected the rose beads that lay on the leaves of **lady's mantel**, for it was believed they possessed special curative powers. It was also well liked in folk medicine.

This perennial plant has a rosette of basal leaves. It thrives in damp areas near streams and marshes. Its straight growing trunk is branched at the top with relatively broad leaves that have shallow, rounded lobes and toothed edges. Their lower blades have a velvety, grey green surface, while those on top are smooth and light green. The pale yellow flowers, which bear an achene fruit, are grouped in cymes forming loose panicles appearing in terminal clusters.

The leaves, which do not have a specific scent, are harvested before the flowering period. They have a slightly bitter and astringent taste. **Lady's mantel** is very conducive to good health because it is rich in vitamin C (five times more than lemon), carotene, mineral salts (calcium, magnesium and phosphorus), mucilage, saponin, bitter substances, salicylic acid and contains up to 8% tannin.

Lady's mantel stimulates digestion, prevents gall bladder obstruction and kidney pain, and also stimulates the production of urine. It is also used to regulate the menstrual period and to relieve menopausal problems. An infusion of the leaves used in a compress helps heal wounds; used as a gargle it soothes swollen glands. In former times, German alchemists believed that a decoction of **lady's mantel** leaves had a rejuvenating effect. The fresh leaves can be used in stews and vegetable dishes. They can be added to a pea puree or served as an accompaniment to meat dishes. A rich beverage can also me made by soaking the fresh leaves in hot water.

ALLIUM CEPA   **Onion**
Root vegetable
Family: *Liliaceae*
Origin: *Asia*
Height: *from 12 to 24 inches (30 to 60 cm)*
Flowering: *July to August*
Properties: *anti-scurvy, antiseptic, cardiotonic, diuretic, emollient, laxative, stimulant*

Onions, relatives of the garlic plant, are amongst the oldest of cultivated plants, and have long been used as a vegetable and a seasoning. The Ancient Egyptians were fond of it, as were the Greeks who blamed it for

being the cause of bad breath. During the Middle Ages, **onions** were found in every kitchen and are still widely used today.

This biennial plant has a largely developed bulb. Its dark green, hollow, tubular leaves swell at the base to form the underground, fleshy bulb. The green or pink flowers are clustered in spherical, terminal umbels on stalks that can reach up to 31 inches (80 cm). The roots of the bulb are poorly ramified appearing in numerous tiny white filaments.

Onions are grown from seed and sown directly onto the field, or raised in greenhouses, and require a soil which is both porous and nutritious. The bulb is usually harvested the same year as the seed was sown, although it is possible to overwinter the plants and thus achieve a second year's cultivation. Once the bulbs are pulled out, they are left to dry in the air for a few days, which facilitates their preservation.

There are two types of **onions**: those large bulb varieties, some of which are pungent and others which are mild, with colors ranging from yellow, to red or white, and which include the small onions often used for pickling; and the small spring **onions**, or scallions, which are eaten whole while they are still young and tender. The taste of **onions** is more or less sweet or pungent, while the characteristic scent results from the sulphur-rich volatile oil they contain which, when released, is an irritant and often brings tears to the eyes of whoever is preparing them.

Because **onions** contain a lot of water, carbohydrates, sugar, mineral salts, lipids, trace elements, vitamins A, B, C, E, and bioflavonoids, they stimulate the cardio-vascular system, fight infections and prevent scurvy. They cleanse and tonify the organism, and alleviate coughs.

A raw **onion** cut in half is used to eliminate the smell of a freshly painted piece of furniture or surface, to remove the rust from a kitchen knife or to reanimate someone who has fainted.

Onion

Onions can be eaten raw in salads, where the addition of nuts and oranges provides a contrast in aroma, and sweetens their taste while reducing their pungency. Cooked onions are used to make delicious toppings for soups, juicy purees, and savory pies and tarts. They can also be stuffed and served as a light dish. Sliced and sautéed, they are used to accompany both red meat and poultry. Peeled and whole, they make a wonderful garnish for roasts. As a chutney or simply pickled, they are often served warm or cold to accompany grilled, sautéed or cold meats. The pungency also offers an interesting contrast to various cheeses. Nevertheless, they can sometimes be difficult to digest.

ALLIUM PORUM — Leek

Stem vegetable
Family: *Liliaceae*
Origin: *Mediterranean area*
Height: *about 19 inches (50 cm)*
Flowering: *May to July*
Properties: *apéritif, diuretic, emollient, purgative*

Leeks do not actually have a genuine bulb, but rather a leaf tuber. The plant has been cultivated since ancient times and is most probably the descendant from another variety of **leek** known as *Allium ampeloprasum*. It was widely used by the Athenians and the Romans for to its beneficial health properties. In the Middle Ages, a very popular soup made with **leeks** was served at just about every table.

Leeks have a white, fleshy compressed stem plate; the thick leaf bases overlap and are arranged concentrically in a nearly cylindrical bulb. A tuft of fibrous, shallow, white roots grows from the base of the stem plate. As the plant develops, a tall solid stalk arises bearing light or dark green, sometimes slightly violet, leaves and a large globular umbel with many white, pink and violet, star shaped flowers. The plant has a sweet fragrance that attracts insects; thereby, promoting pollination of neighboring species. **Leeks** are propagated from seed in deep, rich and permeable soil; this is done either in March in the greenhouse or in May in the open field. The young plants are then replanted in rows. Their roots and leaves are, however, first cut back in order to promote growth. Plants sown in March are harvested in August (**autumn leeks**), while those sown in May are harvested from autumn until winter (**winter leeks**). **Winter leeks** are biennial since they only bloom the following spring. However, some shoots are left untouched in order to promote seed production.

Leeks contain only a few calories, but much water and many mineral salts such as iron, magnesium, calcium, potassium, phosphorus and sulphur. Furthermore, they are rich in mucilage, cellulose, as well as vitamins A, B and C, which are to be found in the green parts of the plant. This vegetable stimulates digestion, soothes inflammations of the larynx, tracheitis, and bronchitis. Its juice clears the voice. This vegetable has become the national emblem of Wales. It is known to have been displayed as a Welsh emblem in 1536 and in **Henry V**, **Shakespeare** acknowledged this as an ancient custom. One legend tells of a battle between the Welsh and the Saxons fought in a field of **leeks**. At some time in the past, the **leek** was an important part of the diet but it is not commonly eaten today. It is delicious when part of the traditional **leek** and **potato** soup.

AMARANTUS CAUDATUS　　　　　　**Amaranth**
Fruit vegetable
Family: *Amaranthaceae*
Origin: *Latin America*
Height: *3 to 8 feet (1 to 2.50 m)*
Flowering: *late spring*
Properties: *nourishing, invigorating*

A very old herbaceous plant, **amaranth** was already grown as a cereal more than 4,000 years ago on the high plateaus of the Andes; in Africa and Asia it is still considered a nutritional plant. There are about 60 varieties which are cultivated as vegetables and cereals in tropical and subtropical regions of the world.

This hairy, strong, fast growing plant has a well ramified foliage with alternate, oval, leaves. Its very small, monoecious, reddish to magenta-red flowers appear in long hanging clusters which can reach up to 12 inches (30 cm) long. They bear numerous very small, reddish brown seeds rich in starch. **Amaranth** is propagated from seed on well permeable, light soil. Containing starch, proteins, sugar, vitamin A and mineral salts, it is a very nutritional vegetable and very easy to digest.

Its crushed seeds are used to produce a starch used in porridges, pastries, crepes, and biscuits flavored with ginger. Its leaves are used as any other green vegetable in soups, gratins, herbal pâtés, stuffings and omelettes. They are also used as a side dish for meat or fish. Its flowers, which keep their color when dry, are used to make dried bouquets. **Amaranth** is considered a symbol of immortality.

AMORPHOPHALLUS　　　**Elephant's foot**
CAMPANULATUS　　**or Hottentot bread**
Root vegetable
Family: *Araceae*
Origin: *Africa and tropical Asia*
Height: *6 feet (1.80 m)*
Flowering: *spring*
Properties: *nutritional, mineralizing*

Elephant's foot, also known as **hottentot bread**, belongs to the family of the *Araceae*, and is cultivated in the tropics because of its enormous edible tuber. It is grown mostly in tropical Asia and the Pacific region.

It is a herbaceous, monocotyledon, twining plant with a few gigantic petioled leaves. It has a hardy, large, woody and partially exposed tuber covered with voluminous tubercules resembling an **elephant's foot** and weighing about 55 lbs. (25 kg). The flowers, generally small and inconspicuous, are surrounded by a spathe. There is another variety *Amorphophallus titanum* which has the largest flowers of the vegetable kingdom: its leaves can reach a length of 6.5 ft. (2 m) and a diameter of up to 4 ft. (1.20 m). Fruitage is insignificant due to the fact that the fruit very rarely develop to full maturity. The tubers have a very mild, slightly pungent taste. Its culture takes place by planting the tubers in damp, rich soil in tropical regions. Harvesting is done very carefully because both plant and tubers contain calcium oxalate which causes skin irritation. The tubers are stored dry and in the dark. The large amount of calcium oxalate contained in the tubers is removed by soaking or cooking. **Elephant's foot** is rich in starch, fiber, carbohydrates, proteins, mineral salts (calcium, potassium), and vitamins A, B and C. It is a very nutritious vegetable which provides the organism with the necessary minerals and vitamins.

Elephant's foot must be peeled using gloves. After that, the tubers are soaked for a whole day in water that is constantly changed. Subsequently, they can be cut into pieces and fried, mashed into a puree, or simply cooked in water. They can be used to prepare porridges, ragouts and soup stocks. A starch is extracted from the

---

Leek

Young leeks have a sweet taste and are eaten raw with salt. Cooked, they are delicious with a vinaigrette. Leeks are used to prepare vegetable pies, purees, soufflés and stews. They can also be cooked in water, rolled with ham, topped with a béchamel sauce, covered with cheese and baked in the oven like a gratin. They can also be cut in slices and sautéed in butter to accompany meat, game or fish.

tubers and used in desserts, cakes, and soup vermicelli. The young leaves are steamed and eaten like **asparagus**. Tubers and leaves are also used as animal fodder.

APIUM GRAVEOLENS VAR. DULCE   *Celery*
Stem vegetable
Family: Umbelliferae
Origin: Mediterranean basin
Height: 20 to 24 inches (50 to 60 cm)
Flowering: summer (from the second year)
Properties: apéritif, purifier, digestive, diuretic, tonic

Celery was used as a flavoring by the ancient Egyptians, Greeks and Romans. The ancient form resembled smallage or wild **celery** and it was used among other things in funeral ceremonies. Over time, the quality and taste of smallage was improved through cultivation. In the 17th century, it became a very popular nutritional plant known in Italy as **celery**. During the Renaissance, **celery** made its way to France where the new vegetable with its juicy, tender leafstalks began to be cooked as a vegetable and used as a flavoring. Today, there are several varieties of **celery**, like the Pascal, whose fleshy, succulent leaves are used in salads.

Celery is a plant with strong branches and bright green foliage. The plant has large, fleshy, upright leafstalks, also known as petioles, which are grouped on one unique stem with small roots. The white, umbel flowers appear once the plant is two years old.

Celery is cultivated in rich soil in open land with a good irrigation system. The seeds are sown in April, and in June the seedlings are replanted leaving a space of 12 inches (30 cm) between each one. After the fresh young shoots have been harvested in summer the plant is blanched (i.e., deprived of light) to produce light tender shoots. There are, however, varieties that blanch naturally. The last shoots must be pulled before the frost begins; **celery** does not prosper in the cold. They should be stored in a cellar, where they will keep for a longer period. **Celery** leafstalks are crisp, juicy, slightly peppery with a characteristic strong aroma.

The nutritional value of **celery** is low, hardly containing any fat and proteins. The water content amounts to approximately 90%, and it is rich in fiber. It also contains carotene, vitamins A and C. Because it contains vitamin E, it is said to be an aphrodisiac. Its essential oil strengthens the digestive system. It is also a vegetable that helps the body eliminat toxins. The juice

of the pressed leaves also have a soothing effect on rheumatism.

The seeds have a strong aroma and a slightly bitter taste. They can be used whole, or ground to a powder and used as a seasoning for salads, soups and stews, fish dishes, various sauces or **tomato** juice. In Scandinavia they are used to season bread dough. **Celery salt**, a mixture of ground **celery** seeds and salt, has a brownish color and a rather intensive taste, and should therefore be used sparingly when seasoning food. **Celery** also keeps for a long time when stored in the fridge (particularly when wrapped in aluminium foil).

APIUM GRAVEOLENS   *Celeriac*
VAR. RAPACEUM   *or Celery root*
Root vegetable
Family: Umbelliferae
Origin: Mediterranean basin
Height: 12 inches (30 cm)
Flowering: summer (from the second year)
Properties: apéritif, aromatic, diuretic, stimulant, stomachic, tonic

---

In contrast to celery, **celeriac** has little foliage and a voluminous root tuber. **Celeriac** is the result of several attempts to improve wild celery by reducing the number of flowers and further developing its stalks and roots.

Even though **celeriac** was already known in Italy during the 16th century, it took almost two centuries for it to make it to the tables of the rest of Europe. In England it was only introduced in the 19th century via Alexandria.

Essentially, it consists of a large, white, relatively smooth edible root tuber which can weigh more than 2.2 lbs. (1 kg). The plant is crowned by bright green leaves with hard, thick stalks. On the base of the tuber there are small radicles. Its taste is very strong and slightly peppery. It is cultivated from seed, initially indoors at the beginning of the spring, and later in the open, in temperate regions on neutral soil; too much fertilizer easily causes the tuber to dry up. It should, however, be watered regularly. In the middle of summer, the first still tender and sweet tubers can be harvested. However, the real harvest takes place in late August before temperatures drop. To protect the plants from frost, they are covered with a layer of straw. **Celeriac** can be stored in a cool, dry, dark cellar for a long time.

Celery

Celery is eaten raw in salads such as salad niçoise. It can also be served as an hors d'œuvre, raw, cut into small pieces and served along with a dip. Its strongly aromatic leaves are used in preparing stocks and soups. It can be pickled in vinegar and used as a seasoning. It can be boiled in water or steamed to accompany meat, or prepared as a gratin with béchamel sauce and grated cheese on top. Celery is also used in vegetable soups, with fish and seafood.

In contrast to celery, **celeriac** is poor in vitamin C, but contains numerous trace elements such as bromine, copper, iron, iodine, manganese, magnesium and zinc, as well as carbohydrates and great amounts of cellulose. It has hardly any fat or proteins. It is a nutritional vegetable which provides lots of energy and has important medical properties. It increases the synthesis of certain hormones, it stimulates the metabolism and digestion, and is also a diuretic.

ARCTIUM LAPPA — Burdock
Leaf and root vegetable
Family: Compositae
Origin: Europe and Asia
Height: 5 to 6 feet (1.60 to 1.80 m)
Flowering: July to August
Properties: anti-poison, bactericide, purifier, diuretic, regulates blood sugar, stomachic, sudorific

---

In Antiquity, **burdock** was only used for its medicinal properties. During the Middle Ages, the plant was said to help the growth of hair. It is also said that **Henry III of France** was cured of a terrible skin disease with its leaves. Once it had spread throughout Europe and Asia, it made its way to America.

This hardy biennial plant is easily recognizable due to its seeds which tend to hook onto the fur of animals and people's clothing. It has a pivotal, fleshy, ramified root, outside brown and inside white, which becomes fibrous with maturity.

Burdock thrives on ground rich in nitrogen in temperate and northern subtropical regions. During the first year, a rosette of large basal leaves appears. In the second year, a tall, hairy, ramified, cottonlike, reddish trunk develops. Its entire, oval, alternate, leaves with basal petioles, are covered on the underside by a light grey fuzz. Its purple-red flowers appear in loose corymbs with large, globular peduncles surrounded by green bracts provided with tiny pointed hooks that adhere to rough surfaces. These flowers bear brown-red to black achenes arranged in several rows.

The root has a sticky, slightly bitter, sweet-and-sour taste. The leaves also have a sticky taste, but they are more sweet and herbaceous. The leaves are harvested during the entire growth period, while the roots are harvested young in the autumn of the first year or in the spring of the following year. **Burdock** is highly perishable; therefore, it must be consumed immediately.

Because its leaves contain a lot of vitamin C, they are an excellent tonic; they are used during convalescence and in health spas. The root contains inulin, a substance which replaces sugar in the cases of diabetes, as well as proteins, carbohydrates, mucilage, tannin, resin, bitter substances, ethereal oil, and minerals such as calcium, potassium and phosphorus. In traditional medicine, **burdock** is used to treat kidney problems, urinary tract infections, digestive problems, gastritis, stomach ulcers, eczema, and wounds. Applied in a poultice, the leaves soothe the pain and inflammation caused by insect bites. Steeped in oil, they are used in the manufacture of hair care products.

ASPARAGUS OFFICINALIS — Asparagus
Stem vegetable
Family: Liliaceae
Origin: the Middle East, Mediterranean basin
Height: 3.5 to 5 feet (1 to 1.50 m)
Flowering: spring
Properties: mineralizing, diuretic, purifier, sedative

Asparagus was prized as a vegetable by epicures in Egypt, Byzantium, Greece and Rome. It was introduced to France as late as the 16th century by the **Medicis**. Later **Louis XIV** hired an agronomist, **La Quintinie**, to supervise the gardens of Versailles where fruit and vegetables were grown to please the king. From then on, **asparagus** became quite popular in Europe. Around 1805 it began to be cultivated intensely in the area of Argenteuil which soon became the French **asparagus** capital, producing a white **asparagus** prized for its delicate flavor. Today, **asparagus** is cultivated in almost all temperate regions of the world.

Asparagus is an erect or climbing, dioecious, perennial plant. Its tuberous or rhizome-like roots give rise to a conspicuous, fleshy, feathery spray of branchlets whose true leaves are reduced to small scales gathered in bundles of three or four enclosed by several stipules. Its flowers are small and greenish. Only female flowers bear fruit; small berries, at first green but turning red with maturity, enclosing the seeds. Male plants are stronger and more productive.

Asparagus has a fresh, mild and delicately sweet taste. It is grown in deep, loose, light clay soils with much organic matter, and light, sandy loams which should be broken up regularly with compost and fertilizer. The **asparagus** field is prepared by heaping up

Burdock

The fresh leaves are used to prepare mild and delicious salads. They are also used as an ingredient in spicy, juicy vegetable stews, herbal pâtés and green vegetable gratins. The raw roots can be grated and added to salads and hors-d'œuvres. They are also mixed into various vegetable dishes, stuffings and sauces. In Japan and China the roots are cut into pieces to accompany several fish or meat dishes. They are also crystallized in honey to make a type of confectionery.

earth to form long ridges on top of which narrow shallow trenches are made. **Asparagus** is propagated from seed in early spring directly into the trenches or in May through root division. Harvesting is done three years later in May and June when the seedlings just break through the heaped up earth. They are dug out and cut off at a depth of about 6 inches (15 cm) from the top. Afterwards the earth is reheaped over them. In order for the plants to be productive for about 15 years, they must be fertilized annually. Once cut, **asparagus** can be stored for several days in boxes, or covered with dry peat in a well aired, cool and dark place. It can also be pickled.

Asparagus contains plenty of water and is rich in fiber which makes it easy to digest. It also contains essential oils, sugar, mineral salt (potassium and magnesium), amino acids and trace elements (iron, iodine and copper); however, it is poor in vitamins. It is reputed for its sleep-promoting and sedative effect. Its active substance, asparagin, makes it an excellent diuretic. **Asparagus** slows heart rhythm. In ancient times it was used to prepare a diuretic known as "syrup of five roots." Near Cahors, in the south of France, there is a wild variety of **asparagus**, *Asparagus acutifolius*, which is harvested in April. It has a delicate, stronger taste than that of cultured **asparagus** and it is prepared in the same way.

Asparagus

Before cooking it, asparagus must be peeled with caution because it is very fragile. It can be eaten hot, lukewarm or cold. There are white, purple and green varieties. This last one is the most popular. Asparagus contains many vitamins. Steamed or boiled in salt water, asparagus is served fresh as an hors -d'œuvre or in a spicy aspic as a garnish. It can be prepared with chopped hard boiled eggs, parsley, or with melted butter and covered with bread crumbs. Cooked whole, it can be prepared with eggs, or cut into pieces, it provides a good filling for an omelette.
It can be used to make a gratin covered with bread crumbs, cream, and paprika or Mornay sauce and parmesan cheese. It can also be served as a vegetable alongside white meat and fish. Asparagus is also good in soufflés, purees and soups. Its foliage is often used as a fragrant foliage in floral bouquets.

ATRIPLEX HORTENSIS   **Orach**
Leaf vegetable
Family: *Chenopodiaceae*
Origin: *central Asia*
Height: *5 feet (1.50 m)*
Flowering: *July to September*
Properties: *purifier, diuretic, laxative*

Wild orach, like *Atriplex astata* and *Atriplex patula*, are very ancient, aromatic, edible plants which propagate in dry areas. In antiquity the people of the Mediterranean ate **orach** as a vegetable. In the Middle Ages it was considered an ornamental plant. **Wild orachs** are the true ancestors of three current varieties: one with pale green leaves, another with dark green leaves, and the third with reddish-violet leaves. **Garden orach** was widely grown from the Middles Ages up to the 19th century. Today, it is becoming fashionable once again.

Orach is a splendid herbaceous plant with a somewhat branched stem. Its alternate leaves, triangular and angular, are covered with minuscule glandular hairs which give it a pubescent appearance. The red or yellow flowers appear grouped in numerous interrupted bunches bearing a multitude of flat fruit. It self-propagates from seed, in rows, on fertile, damp soil in the full sun at the beginning of spring or autumn. The young leaves can be harvested three months later and throughout the season; if the shoots grow higher than 20 inches (50 cm) the leaves become too hard. Blanched and frozen, the leaves can be stored for up to a year. Although reminiscent of **spinach** its taste is milder and more delicate because the leaves contain less oxalic acid. **Orach** is rich in calcium, phosphorus, magnesium, iron, vitamin C, carotene, proteins, carbohydrates and anthocyanin (a coloring substance present only in the red variety). It facilitates digestion, purifies the blood, helps cleanse the kidneys and the gall bladder.

Its leaves are prepared like **spinach**: raw, in salads; cooked, in soups and purees. They can also be served as a vegetable sautéed in butter as an accompaniment to meat. The leaves are also used to prepare pies and soufflés. In the garden, it is a very decorative plant.

AVENA SATIVA   **Oat**
Fruit vegetable
Family: *Gramineae*
Origin: *western Asia, the Middle East and Northern Europe*
Height: *4.3 feet (1.30 m)*
Flowering: *spring*
Properties: *emollient, regulates blood sugar, nutritious, sedative, stimulant*

Oat is an annual cereal, cultivated since antiquity, which is probably a descendant of **wild oat** (*Avena fatua*) known for the quality and size of its grains. It reached Middle Europe from Asia Minor during the Bronze Age. Although **oats** are used chiefly as livestock feed, some are processed for human consumption. There are two varieties: *Avena nuda*, which has small grains; and *Avena orientalis* with big, white starchy grains, which is usually preferred for cultivation. The plant thrives in the cool, temperate regions of Northern Europe and it is also grown in Canada and the United States.

The **oat** plant is a tufted annual grass with a hairy, rounded stalk that contains nodes. Its alternate leaves are long, thin and erect. The seeds appear in loose clusters of numerous branches, each bearing florets (ears) that contain the seeded fruit which do not fall off when mature. Its cultivation is done in temperate, humid regions in moist, fertilized soil; the plant does not prosper in dry, arid lands. **Spring oats** are sown in March, while **winter oats** are sown in September.

This cereal is very nutritious. Its grains are high in starch, lecithin, proteins, lipids, sugar, mineral salts such as phosphorus, calcium, magnesium. They are also a source of vitamins A and B. The grain husks contain saponin and its straw is rich in silicon and vitamin A. The whole plant can be used.

Oatmeal is a popular, digestible food for children and during convalescence. The grains have an anti-inflammatory effect, lower cholesterol level and stimulate the metabolism.

In former times, the husks were used as filling for pillows and mattresses, and the starch was used to starch collars and garments. **Oats** are used by dermatologists in a variety of skin products because of their soothing properties.

Oat stalks can also be used to decorate dried flower arrangements. The grains are used to feed fowl, rabbits and horses. **Oats** are used to feed cows because they stimulate milk production.

Oat

Oats are processed to produce flour and several breakfast foods made from rolled oats and the groats. Oat flour is used to make cakes, biscuits with dried raisins, crepes with orange flower, and vanilla or chocolate puddings. Oat semolina cooked in milk is used to prepare desserts with fruit or caramel sauces. Rolled oats are used, when cooked in milk, to prepare porridge which can be served with sugar, almonds, honey, or fruit such as apples, bananas, and oranges cut into pieces. This preparation makes an excellent and very nutritious breakfast. The groats are used not only to make sweet desserts, but also savory and hearty sauces which can be used warm or cold with meat, fish and seafood.

BASELLA RUBRA **Malabar-spinach**
Leaf vegetable
Family: *Basellaceae*
Origin: *tropical regions, India*
Height: *3 to 20 feet (1 to 6 m)*
Flowering: *spring*
Properties: *soothing, purgative, refreshing, mineralizing*

The **Malabar-spinach** is an herbaceous vine which prospers only in moist, warm climate zones. Today it is cultivated extensively as a green vegetable in South-East Asia and Africa.

It is acopious perennial climber which branches out widely. Its alternate leaves are thick, oval or round, pale green with a hint of red. The tiny white or pink flowers are hermaphrodite; their cupshape calyx has five stamens attached to the spathe from the base. They bear small, drupe-like, black, smooth, fleshy fruit which are also surrounded by sepals. The leaves of the **Malabar-spinach** have an insipid, sticky and slightly sour taste. The first harvest takes place six months after sowing on rich, moist soil. The plant is also propagated through its aerial roots which can take root in the earth producing an offspring that is later separated from the parent plant.

This vegetable is a good source of vitamin A, carotene, carbohydrates, starch, mineral salts like calcium, magnesium and iron as well as vitamins B1, B2 and E. **Malabar-spinach** soothes the stomach, strengthens and invigorates the organism. Thanks to its mucilage content, it is a good aid to digestion.

Malabar-spinach is eaten raw, in simple salads, or cooked. Like **spinach** it can be used to compliment other foods. The leaves can be prepared in stews, gratins and soufflés.

BENINCASA HISPIDA **Wax pumpkin**
Fruit vegetable
Family: *Cucurbitaceae*
Origin: *Asia*
Height: *6.5 to 10 feet (2 to 3 m)*
Flowering: *summer*
Properties: *soothing, laxative, sedative, vermifuge (grains)*

This herbaceous plant is a strong climber which, unlike most species of its type, is consumed as a vegetable in tropical regions.

Wax pumpkin is covered by a soft fuzz with thin ground tendrils divided into three parts growing from the bottom of its stalk. Its large, round, palmately lobed leaves are velvety on the top side and covered with tiny bristles. Single, yellow bell-shaped flowers with five lanceolate, dented sepals, appear on the axiles of the leaves. They bear big fleshy, elongated oval, bluish grey to greenish fruit which can reach up to 16 inches (40 cm) in length and about 4 inches (10 cm) in width. They are covered by a waxy substance and filled with flat, oval grains.

The pulp of the fruit is delicious, very light, slightly floury, somewhat like a cross between a **cucumber** and a **pumpkin**.

In Europe the culture of the **wax pumpkin** is difficult because it does not tolerate temperatures below 59 °F (15 °C); nevertheless, in the south of France, it is grown in open fields near the Loire. The plants need a rich, well irrigated soil and sunny exposure.

Plants must be propped in order to ventilate the fruit. Once harvested, the fruit can be kept for a up to a year when stored in a cool, dry place.

Wax pumpkins are also known as English winter melons. They contain a lot of water, but few fatty acids and sugar. They are also a good source of vitamins A and C and trace elements. It is a very nutritious and easily digestible vegetable. Its grains are used to treat worm infestation.

Wax pumpkin is used to prepare soups, purees, gratins and soufflés. Cut in cubes and sautéed, it is a good accompaniment to meat dishes. It is also used in beef, pork and fish stuffings.

BETA VULGARIS
VAR. CICLA
Chard
or Swiss chard
Leaf vegetable
Family: Chenopodiaceae
Origin: Europe
Height: 28 inches (70 cm)
Flowering: summer
Properties: soothing, anti-anaemia, emollient, laxative

Swiss chard is a variety of the **beet** from the Mediterranean region and the Atlantic coast, also known in India. It was first discovered by the Assyrians at around 700 BC. Later, the Greeks and the Romans consumed its leaves just like those of **spinach**; hence its name: **Roman spinach**. In the Middle Ages, **Swiss chard** was used as an ingredient for soups and purees.

Swiss chard has greatly developed leaves and leafstalks. The leaves, which have a fleshy texture and are slightly pleated, are smooth, dark green, and veined. The small flowers develop numerous irregularly formed fruit with several hollow cavities, each one containing a seed.

Swiss chard has a juicy and refreshing taste. It is grown from seed between April and May on rich, moist soil. Harvesting takes place two months later and continues well into the autumn. The stems have a delicate flavor. Cooked and chilled stems are very good with salad dressing or mayonnaise.

Chard is a very nutritious vegetable and a good source of iron and vitamins A, B2 and C. It is low in calories and protects against infections of the digestive system and stimulates the metabolism.

Beets
Before preparing this vegetable, the stems must be cut into pieces in order to eliminate the hard fibrous parts. Then they can be boiled in salted water and prepared in a gratin, covered with béchamel sauce and sprinkled with parmesan cheese on top. Cooked in butter, they can be served as a vegetable alongside meat or fowl. The leaves, like spinach, are used in salads, soups or purees. They are also suitable for making soufflés, cakes, gnocchi, stuffing or to be used as a filling for an omelette. They are an ingredient in the poitevin-herbs stuffing which is typical of French cuisine. There is a variety of beet with shiny red and pink stems which is used as an ornamental plant in the garden. In the kitchen they are used in the same way as the white variety, they tend however, to lose their intense color with cooking.

BETA VULGARIS
VAR. ESCULENTA
Beetroot
or Garden beet
Root vegetable
Family: Chenopodiaceae
Origin: Europe
Height: 8 to 12 inches (20 to 30 cm)
Flowering: summer
Properties: apéritif, laxative, mineralizing, stimulant, tonic

---

There are three different types of **beets** cultivated for different purposes: **sugar beet**, **chard** and **beetroot**. The last was already consumed in the Middle Ages in Germany and France, where it quickly became a basic ingredient for many dishes. In the 19th century, it arrived in Russia where it immediately became popular. Today **beetroot** is cultivated in the north of France and in England. **Beetroot** is highly prized for its sugar content and the intense red color.

Beetroot has globular and somewhat conical taproots which can be red to red-purple and flat toward the bottom. The fine, smooth purple red rind encloses a thick flesh, of the same color, covered with concentric ring fibers around the root axis. The tall, branched reddish-brown stems bear clusters of minute green flowers and carry splendid entire, shinny green, red veined leaves. The fruit, or seedballs, contain two to four seeds that appear clustered together. The red color of **beetroot** comes from the anthocyanin pigment it contains and its characteristic pleasant sweet taste is from the active substance, beta carotene. **Beetroot** is cropped in rows from the end of March until May in rich, well fertilized soil. The young plants are thinned out at a distance of 12 inches (30 cm) well protected from the cold which causes them to germinate too early. The harvest takes place in October and November. The roots should be harvested before the frost period and stored in a dark, cool place.

Beetroot is a very nutritious vegetable. It contains a lot of water and fiber. It is relatively poor in vitamin C, but is a good source of vitamins B1, B2, B3, B6 and E, carotene, iron, sodium, calcium, magnesium, phosphorus and potassium.

Because **beetroot** contains glutamic acid and beta carotene, it strengthens the functioning of the brain and stimulates the balance of hepatic cells. Because of the vitamins it contains, it helps prevent viral infections.

BRASSICA CHINENSIS — Bok choy or Chinese mustard

Leaf vegetable
Family: Cruciferae
Origin: the Far East
Height: 12 to 20 inches (30 to 50 cm)
Flowering: summer
Properties: anti-diarrhoea, anti-inflammatory, stimulant, tonic

Bok choy is relatively new to Europe. In Asia, this **cabbage** of the **mustard family** is more popular than **cabbage** itself. It is one of the least common **Chinese cabbages** and the one with the most atypical characteristics.

There are two kinds: **bok choy** which resembles a **leek**, and the **tientsin** with its big, fleshy, almost unveined leaves.

The plant is formed by a rosette of entire leaves with slightly undulated edges which are glossy dark green. It has thick, crisp white stalks in a loose head. The root is small and delicate. It is usually cultivated in humid, warm regions, but there are a few varieties which are suitable for cultivation in temperate zones because they are rather more tolerant of cold temperatures. The sowing takes place from February to March in the greenhouse. Later the seedlings are replanted at intervals of 5 inches (15 cm) from each other. At the end of September, the rosettes are harvested by cutting them at a height of less than an inch (2 cm) from the ground. New rosettes will then sprout from the rootstock. In Asia **Bok choy** is stored in sand, salt or vinegar. In Europe it is either stored in the cellar or soaked in water and kept wrapped in a moist cloth in the refrigerator.

Bok choy is rich in vitamin C, carotene, potassium and proteins. It has a invigorating effect on the organism. It helps fight anaemia and relieves inflammations and diarrhoea.

Beetroot

Small, young beetroot can be eaten raw. It can also be pickled and used as a relish or grated into a salad. Boiled and cut in small cubes, it can be served with a vinaigrette as an hors-d'œuvre. Beetroot is the ingredient in the typical Russian soup known as borscht. It can also be used to prepare jams and a sweet wine. Cooked in sweetened water, it is a great side dish for game and fowl dishes. Beetroot leaves are used as livestock fodder.

BRASSICA JUNCEA — Brown or Indian mustard

Leaf vegetable
Family: Cruciferae
Origin: Asia
Height: 8 to 12 inches (20 to 30 cm)
Flowering: June
Properties: aromatic, purgative, emetic

This **Himalayan mustard** was introduced approximately one hundred years ago to Europe, appearing first in Hungary and later in other central European countries. Its smooth leaves are pale green, dark green or colored purple, plain or slightly crumpled with fleshy petioles arranged in the form of basal rosettes. The yellow flowers stand in a pedicel which rises approximately 5 feet (1.5 m) above the ground. They bear fruit, or siliques, which contain numerous light brown to dark brown seeds of a bitter, sharp taste.

In order to cultivate **Indian mustard**, seeds must be sown very early in the spring or from July onwards, because when it is sown at the beginning of the summer the plant germinates too early without forming rosettes. In hot regions, it can be cultivated in the open during winter, harvesting the leaves on demand. If the plant has bloomed, the floral peduncles can be harvested as a vegetable. Once the fruit ripens, the seeds are harvested to produce **mustard**. The leaves can be eaten fresh or pickled in vinegar or brine. **Indian mustard** contains mucilage and alkaloids. It improves digestion, invigorates the organism and stimulates all vital functions.

The fresh leaves can be used to prepare a pungent salad, or they can be cooked like **spinach**. Pickled in vinegar, they make a delicious accompaniment or side dish. The fresh flowers can also be used in salads, or cooked and served with a vinaigrette as an accompaniment to other dishes.

BRASSICA NAPUS VAR. NAPOBRASSICA — Rutabaga or Swede turnip

Root vegetable
Family: Cruciferae
Origin: northern hemisphere
Height: 12 to 16 inches (30 to 40 cm)
Flowering: spring
Properties: nutritious, stimulant, tonic

Rutabaga, also known as **swede turnip,** or more commonly just **swede**, is one of the oldest vegetables of the northern hemisphere. Before the introduction of the **potato**, this root was an important ingredient in the European diet. During the 19th century, **swede** was grown in most kitchen gardens throughout the south of France. Thus, it became a synonym for "bad times." Today, **swede** is gaining back its popularity and is once again being sold on markets.

This annual, hardy plant carries big, petioled, bluish leaves which are smooth and glaucous. They are strongly lobed all the way up to the central vein, and appear in a rosette-like bunch at the top of the yellow root. The latter bears a distinct neck with well marked leaf scars and is surrounded by numerous radicles. The yellow flowers have four, cross-shaped petals and four free sepals equal in size which open upon maturity in order to release the seeds. **Swede** has a sweet and slightly pungent taste.

Sowing takes place from March to April directly onto the field. While the plants are developing, they are banked up with soil because the roots tend to come out of the ground. **Swede** is hardy to cold, so harvesting can be done in late autumn. Once harvested, it is piled up and covered with straw and soil in order to preserve it for a longer period of time.

This vegetable is very nutritious and a good source of proteins and carbohydrates. Besides, it contains vitamins B and C as well as traces of sulphur which give it its characteristic pungent taste.

Swede is extensively cultivated, often as a cattle fodder crop.

BRASSICA OLERACEA VAR. ACEPHALA — Kale
Leaf vegetable
Family: Cruciferae
Origin: Europe
Height: 12 inches to 4 feet (30 cm to 1.20 m)
Flowering: late spring (from the second year)
Properties: anti-scurvy, vulnerary, purifier, diuretic

Kale was already cultivated by the Teutons and Celts. The Romans used **kale** for its healing and nutritious qualities. **Kale** is still a widely used vegetable today.

It is a hardy biennial, which, in contrast to most other **cabbages**, does not form a cabbage head. The plant produces a strong growing rosette of long petioled, elongated leaves with wavy to frilled margins. The yellow flowers and the small fruit resemble those of most crucifers. The small, and shallow root makes the plant very fragile. For this reason, dwarf and semi dwarf varieties have been developed.

Kale is one of the hardiest and most undemanding vegetable crops. It can tolerate temperatures as low as –59 °F (–15 °C) and prospers in almost any soil.

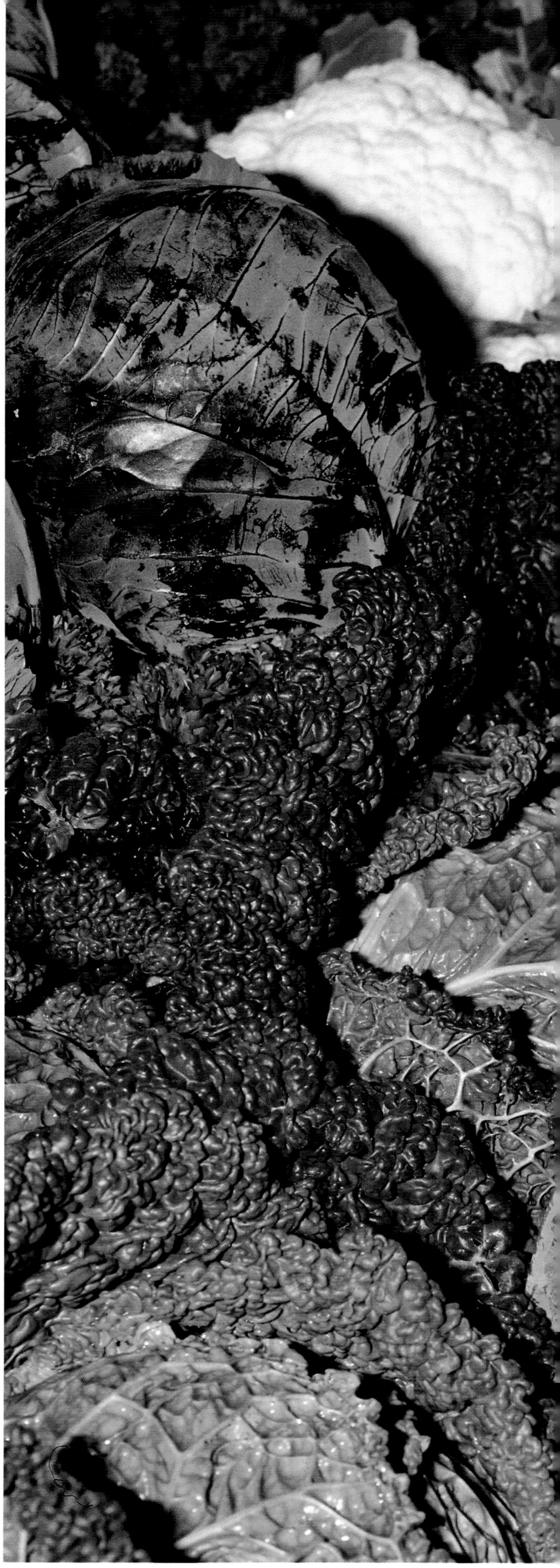

Kale

Kale boiled in water or sautéed in butter is used to accompany both meat and fowl. It can also be used to make purees, soups and gratins. Cooked in the pressure cooker with spices, cream, and hard boiled eggs, it makes a delicious stuffing for fowl. Raw, it is wonderful in a salad with olive oil and lemon juice.

Cauliflower

Cauliflower has a delicious nutty taste when used raw in a salad. It can be pickled in vinegar and used as a condiment. In this way, it is used in the preparation of salad niçoise. It forms part of the popular mixed pickles made in Great Britain. Steamed cauliflower is prepared in a vinaigrette or covered with a light cheese sauce and gratinated. It is also prepared as fritters, purees, and of course, it is used to garnish several meat dishes.

The sowing takes place from April to May directly onto the field. The plant may be harvested by cutting off the entire rosette before the stem has elongated, or (especially in areas with long, cool growing periods) the individual lower leaves may be removed progressively as the main stem elongates.

Kale which is harvested after the first frost is slightly sweeter in taste. The leaves of **kale** contain

protein, sugar, fiber and are a good source of vitamin C, particularly during the winter. Besides, **kale** is rich in iron and mineral salts.

It is a mineralizing vegetable which detoxifies the body and improves digestion. **Kale** juice is an excellent healing agent for external wounds and its high content of vitamin C helps the body fight against all sorts of infections and fatigue.

BRASSICA OLERACEA   *Cauliflower*
VAR. BOTRYTIS
Flower vegetable
Family: Cruciferae
Origin: the Middle East
Height: 16 to 24 inches (40 to 60 cm)
Flowering: summer
Properties: soothing, anti-scurvy, antiseptic, purifier, diuretic

Cauliflower is one of the oldest vegetables known in France, which is one of its main producers. It is grown in the regions of Brittany, the Nord-Pas-de-Calais, Normandie and Bouches-du-Rhône.

Cauliflower has a big, thick, woody stem with bluish-green leaves and crisp leaf stalks. Enormous, compact flower peduncles form an imposing white terminal head made up of uniform white, tight bouquets. This infertile inflorescence is, in fact, a vegetable monstrosity.

Cauliflower is grown from seed. Once developed, the young plants are replanted at a distance of 16 inches (40 cm) apart from each other. They must be watered and fertilized regularly if they are to form magnificent heads. Harvesting takes place from late spring until winter. Cauliflower can be kept covered with a moist cloth in the refrigerator for a few days. It can also be frozen once it has been blanched. The vegetable is not very nutritious; it contains a lot of water and some sulphur, vitamins A, B and C. However, cauliflower is rich in fiber and mineral salts. It has small amounts of carbohydrates and mucilage and very little fat.

Cauliflower is good for the skin, the bones, the liver and the nervous system.

BRASSICA OLERACEA VAR. CAPITATA **Cabbage**
Leaf vegetable
Family: Cruciferae
Origin: the Middle East
Height: 16 inches (40 cm)
Flowering: late spring (from the second year)
Properties: antibacterial, anti-scurvy, diuretic

It is said that this vegetable was already bred in Antiquity from the wild, or sea cabbage, found on the coasts of the Atlantic Ocean and the Mediterranean Sea. The aim was to obtain a greater number of leaves which were even more serrated. After several rigorous selections, common cabbage and savoy cabbage were developed. These cabbages have smooth leaves and come in two different shapes and three different colors.

The heads of horticultural varieties of cabbage range in shape from pointed, through globular, to flat; from soft to hard in structure; through various shades of green, grey-green, and magenta or red. In Alsace there is a green cabbage, which is pickled to make choucroute,

or as it is known in Germany "sauerkraut." These are very ancient herbal plants.

All these forms of cabbage have a hard head formed by the grouping of entire, smooth, grossly veined leaves and a compact voluminous head with a few external leaves. The entire structure is supported by a deformed stem. The young flowers have four petals and four opposing, cross shaped sepals. They bear fruit known as siliques with two valves which open upon maturity releasing the seeds. There are of course some differences among these cabbages: red cabbage is the smallest one with a more pronounced and pungent taste than that of white cabbage, which has a sweet taste. Both are eaten raw in salads or pickled.

Cabbage is easy to cultivate and is a major table vegetable in most countries of the temperate zone. It can be kept fresh in the refrigerator or frozen after being blanched. Cabbage has a high water content and is rich in carbohydrates, nitrogen and fatty acids. It has few calories and a lot of vitamin C, which is why it is used to prevent scurvy, viral infections and anaemia. Because it contains sulphur derivatives it also has antibacterial properties.

BRASSICA OLERACEA VAR. CYMOSA **Broccoli**
Leaf vegetable
Family: Cruciferae
Origin: Asia Minor
Height: 16 to 20 inches (40 to 50 cm)
Flowering: from autumn to winter
Properties: anti-scurvy, purifier, diuretic

Broccoli cultivation is fairly recent. It was first cultivated in Italy, and then spread to Great Britain where it is consumed in great amounts. This close relative of cauliflower is an annual plant. It is fast growing, upright and bears tight, dense green clusters of flower buds at the ends of the central axis and the branches. Harvesting takes place before the Flowering while the buds are still on the compact, grey-green head. Like cauliflower, broccoli also has a thick, woody trunk with several fleshy pedicels which end in the floral clusters. Its leaves are fleshy, deeply scalloped and bluish-green. However, broccoli has a longer growth period than cauliflower.

It demands a well-irrigated, rich soil, but is hardy to temperature fluctuations and air humidity. The flavor

Broccoli

Broccoli is eaten cooked, in a vinaigrette, in gratins, with light sauces, in fritters and purees. In Italy and Asia it is particularly used as an ingredient for cheese omelettes and for sweet-and-sour pork. On the photograph, broccoli is the vegetable that appears between the peppers.

of **broccoli** resembles that of **cabbage** but is somewhat milder. It has a high water content and is rich in vitamins C and E. It is used to prevent scurvy and its invigorating effect is beneficial during convalescence. It helps cleanse the organism from toxins and improves the digestion.

BRASSICA OLERACEA VAR. GEMMIFERA
Brussels sprouts
Leaf vegetable
Family: Cruciferae
Origin: Belgium
Height: 2.5 to 3 feet (0.80 to 1 m)
Flowering: late spring (from the second year)
Properties: anti-scurvy, diuretic, nutritious, mineralizing

Brussels sprouts appeared on markets around 1820 after a careful cultivation and selection process. They are the smallest type of **cabbage** of the **mustard family**.

The plant's main stem is quite tall with a not very deep flat root. When cultivating the plant care must be taken that it takes root well, because the small heads of the plant, once developed, can pull the plant out of the ground with their weight. To avoid this the plant has to be constantly banked up with earth and sheltered from the wind. The stem has axillary buds along its length which develop into small heads or sprouts similar to heads of **cabbage** but measuring 1 to 2 inches (25 to 40 mm) in diameter.

Brussels sprouts are a slow growing vegetable. It is sown in April in plant beds and transplanted directly onto the field once it is strong enough. **Brussels sprouts** endure neither aridity nor heat. They need a rich soil containing little nitrogen to avoid the heads opening.

Once they are long enough, **Brussels sprouts** heads are separated from the stem, from bottom to top. Harvesting is done during the plant's entire growth period. If they are not harvested regularly, the heads on the lower part of the stem begin to turn yellow. The tops of the plant can also be cut in order to accelerate growth. In order to avoid diseases, yellow leaves should be removed.

Brussels sprouts are hardy to cold and are generally best when harvested before the first frost. There are also red-purple varieties which are less productive, but more tasty. **Brussels sprouts** are the most fragrant and tasty of the **cabbages**. They are also very nutritious containing high amounts of water, vitamin C, mineral salts, carbohydrates and fatty acids.

BRASSICA OLERACEA VAR. GONGYLODES
Kohlrabi
Stem vegetable
Family: Cruciferae
Origin: the Far East
Height: 16 to 20 inches (40 to 50 cm)
Flowering: summer (from the second year)
Properties: invigorating, nutritious

Kohlrabi's most distinctive feature is the greatly enlarged stem just above the soil which is the part of the plant harvested for food. It was developed by gardeners after being crossbred several times.

Its white-green stem is rounded, fleshy and flat at the ends. The length of the stem is covered with long leafstalks with green, pinnately lobed and fragile leaves. The fine, rather narrow root is not anchored very deeply in the soil.

The tuber has, on average, a diameter of approximately 4 inches (10 cm), but it can also reach 12 inches (30 cm) and weigh up to 4.4 lbs. (2 kg).

Kohlrabi can be purple, red-purple or white. It is sown directly onto the field in the spring and must be watered regularly to ensure that it does not become fibrous. Harvesting takes place from early summer until autumn.

The harvested **kohlrabi** is easy to store and keeps fresh very long without losing its properties. It is rich in fiber, mineral salts, trace elements and vitamin C; therefore, it is very nutritious. It is a stimulating and invigorating vegetable. It is a very popular seasonal vegetable which facilitates digestion.

The peeled tuber is boiled in water that is changed several times to eliminate the nitrogen it contains which makes it difficult to digest.

Kohlrabi is used to compliment sausages and pork. Because of its fragrance and flavor, **kohlrabi** can be used in purees and vegetable soups. When raw, because of its sweet mustardy taste, it is an excellent ingredient for salads. It can also be stuffed with meat and prepared as a gratin.

Red cabbage
Raw red cabbage, finely cut, adds color and aroma to salads and raw fruit and vegetables dishes. It can be cooked in a pot with apples or red wine and served as an accompaniment to meat, fowl and game dishes.

Savoy cabbage

Savoy cabbage was discovered towards the end of the Middle Ages. This head **cabbage** has a green head, more or less dense, formed by frilled, wavy leaves that due to their waffle like structure are surmounted and folded one on to the other. It has a deformed stem with a small root. The small yellow flowers bear tiny fruit or siliques containing numerous seeds.

It has a delicate flavor. It is cultivated the whole year long from seed. When it is sown in January / February harvesting takes place before the summer. When grown in the nursery, it is sown in April and harvested from autumn until winter. **Savoy cabbage** is available during the whole year thanks to the different varieties that exist. It is hardy, but requires a soil rich in nutrients which must be well irrigated in the summer because the plant is not tolerant of heat. Storage should be in a dark, cool place.

Savoy cabbage is best when stewed with **carrots** and **potatoes**. Its leaves can be used to make a delicious herbal stuffing for meat or cooked and prepared as a gratin. It is also used in stocks and soups, often served with bacon and croutons.

BRASSICA PEKINENSIS

Chinese or Celery cabbage

Leaf vegetable
Family: Cruciferae
Origin: the Far East
Height: 12 to 20 inches (30 to 50 cm)
Flowering: summer
Properties: anti-anaemia, anti-inflammatory, anti-diarrhoea, mineralizing

Chinese cabbage
Raw Chinese cabbage gives salads a very crisp, refreshing taste and a fine aroma. It is used in soups, broths and ragouts. It can also be sautéed and served to accompany various meat and other vegetable dishes.

Chinese cabbage is the result of the careful crossbreeding of a Chinese garden variety. It was introduced to Europe in the 18th century and soon became one of the most popular **Chinese cabbages**.

Its root is fine and thin; its head pale green and fleshy. Its interlocked leaves have a powdery appearance. They are formed by a large white side with numerous veins and are slightly crinkled and wavy on the edges. **Chinese cabbage** blooms in the summer. After being exposed to too much light, it does not form a head and germinates too early.

Chinese cabbage is a crisp, digestible vegetable with a delicate mustard taste. It is sown in February in the nursery on moist soil. It is harvested at the end of September by cutting off the heads roughly 1 inch (3 cm) from the ground to clear the way for new rosettes. Even in the refrigerator or the cellar, it can be kept for only a short period of time. In Asia it is preserved in salt, in vinegar or dried.

This vegetable contains plenty of water and is rich in vitamin C, carotene, proteins and potassium. Therefore, it works against anaemia and diarrhoea, and helps relieve inflammations.

BRASSICA RAPA

Turnip

Root and leaf vegetable
Family: Cruciferae
Origin: northern hemisphere
Height: 20 inches (40 cm)
Flowering: summer (from the second year)
Properties: tranquilizer, diuretic

Before **potatoes** arrived in Europe, **turnip** was for many years considered to be the vegetable of the poor. Today, it is a fashionable vegetable. It is widely used in England, and in Scotland it is regarded as the national vegetable.

The **turnip** root is formed by the thickening of the primary root of the seedling together with the base of the young stem immediately above it. The leaves, forming a rosette-like bunch at the top of the root, are grass-green and bear rough hairs. In the second season the bud in the center of the rosette forms a strong, erect, branched stem bearing somewhat glaucous smooth leaves somewhat like those of the **swede**. Their color varies according to the species: early ones are generally white or violet around the high part of the tuber; others are yellow, greyish, orange-yellow or even black. Stem and branches end in clusters of small, bright yellow flowers, which are succeeded by smooth, elongated, short-beaked pods containing brown pungent seeds.

Turnip is a vary undemanding vegetable to cultivate. It is sown directly onto the field during the whole

season from March to September. The first tiny **turnips** are so mild and tender that they can be quickly harvested and eaten raw. They can also be harvested once they have fully developed, and are then ready to be cooked.

Turnip is very low in calories, but it contains a lot of water, fiber, essential oils, sugar and mineral salts. It is not very nutritious, but it is used for its diuretic and tranquilizing properties. It is also of use in weight loss diets.

CAMPANULA RAPUNCULUS　　　**Rampion**
Root and leaf vegetable
Family: *Campanulaceae*
Origin: *Europe, Asia, North Africa*
Height: *20 to 31 inches (30 to 80 cm)*
Flowering: *summer (from the second year)*
Properties: *antiseptic, astringent, tranquilizer, mineralizing*

Rampion was eaten in medieval Europe during times of famine. Very soon its nutritional qualities were discovered and it became part of every day menus.

Rampion grew mostly as a weed in vineyards, but was soon also cultivated in kitchen gardens as a vegetable. Today it is cultivated particularly in the south of France and in Italy. It is a beautiful plant with a white, fleshy root which resembles that of the **carrot**. It propagates through numerous, tiny, secondary root tubers. In the course of the first year, it produces narrow stem leaves and untoothed, broadly oval basal leaves that form a rosette around the stalk. During the second year, it produces ascending clusters of long-stalked lilac bells bearing capsules which contain in each case numerous seeds. The root has a soft, sticky, slightly sweet taste. This hardy perennial plant is cultivated by laminar sowing or plantation of the root tubers. It is harvested in autumn and stored in the cellar. The young leaves can also be consumed; they are harvested before the inflorescence forms.

Rampion contains inulin, a sugar substitute. Therefore, it is often used in special dietary foods for diabetics.

In addition, it contains iron, calcium, phosphorus, vitamins, mucilage, cellulose, rubber resin, choline, and mineral salts. This plant also has medicinal properties: it strengthens, invigorates and purifies the organism and is used to treat angina.

The root is used as a vegetable for soups and as an accompaniment to meat dishes. It is also often eaten raw in salads. The leaves can be cooked in the same manner as spinach leaves. Its blue flowers are also very decorative in ornamental gardens.

CAPSICUM ANNUUM　　　**Bell pepper**
Fruit vegetable
Family: *Solanaceae*
Origin: *South and Central America*
Height: *24 to 32 inches (60 to 80 cm)*
Flowering: *May*
Properties: *anti-fatigue, anti-stress, apéritif, digestive*

Bell peppers arrived in Hungary from the New World around 1585. However, the plant which is a spice and a vegetable at the same time, was not introduced into other European countries until about a century ago.

There are more than 200 different species of **peppers**, varying not only in form and color, but also with a wide variety of aromas and tastes. **Bell peppers** are one of the milder variations, and are available in several different colors: red, green, yellow, orange and violet.

This herbaceous plant has branched, woody stems equipped with simple leaves that alternate in gentle colors of green. Its white, self-pollinating flowers bear generally elongated or rounded fruit which are green at first, gradually turning red, orange, yellow, purple or black once they have reached full maturity. The fruit appears in the shape of big smooth, inflated, round or elongated berries. Their interior is formed by lobes which enclose numerous seeds. Their skin is hard, smooth and glossy. Their thick, juicy, sweet or pungent pulp is endowed with a gamut of different flavors. The plants are grown from seed on rich, humid soil and in sunny fields. The plants require warm temperatures and a lot of water. They are sown from February to March in sheltered beds. The young plants are transplanted from the outset of the flowers directly onto the field. Harvesting is mainly done by hand three months later from June until the autumn.

Bell peppers are rich in vitamin C and have a high water content. Ripe **bell peppers** are rich in vitamin A, fiber, carotene, mineral salts, essential oil which give it their characteristic flavor, and coloring substances. This vegetable is beneficial during child-

---

Turnip

Not only the root of the turnip is used in the kitchen. There are some varieties which are cultivated for their fleshy leaves. Cooked in salted water, the young shoots are seasoned in different ways. The leaves can be used in stews or as green vegetables. Raw, they are added to salads to give them a pungent taste. Young turnips with their delicate taste are eaten raw. Cooked and cut into pieces, they can be served with butter to accompany various meat dishes, being an especially good companion for roast duck. They are a delicious ingredient for gratins and purees, and can be used in preparing chicken stew, vegetable and oxtail soups.

hood. It stimulates the appetite and gastric secretions. Furthermore, it aids during convalescence and protects against viral infections.

CARLINA ACAULIS — Carline thistle or Stemless caroline

Flower vegetable
Family: Compositae
Origin: Central Europe
Height: 0.4 inches (1 cm)
Flowering: May to September
Properties: antibacterial, astringent, emollient, vulnerary

This now largely forgotten vegetable, which in some countries is registered as a protected species, was in former times, renowned for its medicinal properties. The plant was named either after **Charlemagne** or **Charles V**. According to the legend an angel appeared to him displaying the plant. The angel then explained that the plant could be used to cure his people of the plague.

Carline thistle is a hardy perennial plant related to **thistle** and **burdock**. This self-propagating plant, with its spiny almost non existent stem, thrives in dry, sandy ground and in sunny locations. **Carline thistle** has a dense head of small, usually pink or purple flowers and green, prickly leaves. It also has spiny stems and flower heads without ray flowers. The flowers bear achenes covered with yellow hairs which open up in feathery umbels double in size. Its thick, red-brown, root contains latex and has a fetid smell. The root is harvested in autumn; the flowers are picked before they bear fruit.

When there is a lot of moisture in the air, the sepals around the flower close up forming a conical capsule that protects the flower. The plant contains inulin, a sugar substitute for diabetics, as well as essential oils, tannin, resin, carlinen (an antibiotic substance) and saponine. It is applied to cure eczema, acne and other skin diseases. Its antibiotic property makes it effective against influenza and feverish viral infections.

Its unripe fruit can be prepared like an **artichoke** – either steamed in salted water and served with vinaigrette, or sautéed in butter with parmesan cheese and garlic, and served with grilled or toasted bread and other vegetables. It can also be stuffed with other vegetables covered with a béchamel or other light white sauce, and then baked in the oven as a gratin.

Bell pepper

Bell peppers are generally added raw to salads. They are also used with other raw vegetables to prepare salad niçoise or a variety of seafood salads. Cooked and cut into pieces, they are an ingredient for several dishes like Ratatouille as well as other Mediterranean dishes made with meat, pork, chicken, crab or squid. They are also used in making minestrone soup, and are a real delicacy when braised with ricotta cheese. Bell peppers lend a special aroma to omelettes and several Spanish dishes such as Paella, while Basque cuisine would be unthinkable without them, their colors reflecting those of the Basque national flag, red and green. They are highly regarded as an ingredient for many Chinese dishes, and are an ever present topping for Italian pizzas. Whole, deseeded peppers, stuffed with meat, vegetables or fish and baked in the oven, are served as a main dish, either warm or cold, right across the Mediterranean basin.

CHAEROPHYLLUM BULBOSUM — Turnip-rooted chervil

Root vegetable
Family: Umbelliferae
Origin: eastern France, Central Europe
Height: 47 inches (1.20 m)
Flowering: June to July (from the second year)
Properties: apéritif, nutritious, stomachic, tonic

The **turnip-rooted chervil**, an ancient vegetable which is becoming more and more popular again of late, is found in Europe, Asia and North America. In the 19th century it arrived in Germany from Hungary and soon spread to Spain where it is cultivated not for its root, but for its aromatic leaves. Depending on the region where it is grown, it is a biennial or a perennial. In the wild, it grows in shady, moist soil, mostly on meadows and in vineyards. During the first year, a rosette of very pinnate leaves, reminiscent to that of **parsley**, appear on the short, yellowish, tuberous, very fleshy, **carrot**-shaped root. During the second year dense, close umbel clusters of white flowers appear on the flower stalks which can reach up to 8 inches (20 cm) in length. The flowers bear double, pointed achenes.

The root of the **turnip-rooted chervil** has a rather floury consistency, and is reminiscent in taste of the chestnut. The plant is grown from seed from September to October in cool, airy but not too moist soil. The first leaf shoots appear in February; the root is harvested as soon as the leaves fade and turn yellow, in July. Once the leaves have been removed, the freshly harvested roots are left out on the field to dry for a couple of days. They are then stored in a cellar or silo, where they will keep until the following spring.

The root of the plant is rich in sugar, vitamins B and C, as well as mineral salts. Raw, grated, or sliced with a vinaigrette, it is delicious and nutritious. The fragrant leaves are used to add aroma to stews and salads.

CHAMAEDOREA ELEGANS — Mountain palm tree

Leaf vegetable
Family: Ceroxyloideae
Origin: Mexico and Colombia
Height: 10 feet (3 m)
Flowering: summer
Properties: nutritious, purgative, mineralizing, tonic

Like other palm trees, the mountain palm tree is also harvested for its **cabbage** palm (that is, the large bud that is formed by the flowers and the leaves at the top of the palm). The **mountain palm tree** forms big bushes of approximately 8 feet (2.50 m) in diameter. The short, tightly packed, trunks grow up to 10 feet (3 m) high. The long, light green, pinnate leaves carry from 20 to 40 oblong, pointed leaflets. Its dioecious flowers are borne on long stems of up to 1 yard in length (1 m). They bear small, round, berries the size of a pea which become black as the leaves of the tree turn orange, a characteristic which accentuates the beauty of this palm tree.

The **mountain palm tree** is propagated through its shoots from which new palm trees develop rapidly. Leaf buds are harvested in the spring, once the plant begins to produce sap; the flower buds are harvested during the Flowering.

Palm **cabbages** are highly perishable, and must be either consumed immediately or preserved. They are mostly available canned. They contain a lot of water, fiber, carbohydrates, some oil and mineral salts.

They are cooked in water and served alone or together with other vegetables to accompany meat and fish. Although highly recommended in the form of vegetable fritters, they can also be served cold with a vinaigrette, as an hors-d'œuvre, or simply mixed in a salad.

Chicory

Chicory can be eaten either raw in salads, or cooked. Quickly sautéed and then tossed in the juices of roasted meat, it becomes an attractive accompaniment for a variety of meat dishes. It can also be lightly boiled in water, wrapped with bacon, covered with béchamel sauce and grated cheese (freshly grated parmesan or cheddar) and then baked in the oven. A fine hors-d'œuvre can be made by separating the leaves and filling them with creamed blue cheese and sprinkled with a little lemon. The extract from a variety of chicory is used to make a strong diuretic beverage. Because the root is rich in inulin (fructose type), the beverage is also used for diabetics.

CHENOPODIUM QUINOA   **Quinoa**
Fruit and Leaf vegetable
Family: *Chenopodiaceae*
Origin: *the Andes (Peru, Bolivia and Ecuador)*
Height: *5 feet (1.50 m)*
Flowering: *spring*
Properties: *anti-anaemia, emollient, mineralizing*

Quinoa is a very old plant cultivated for over 3,000 years on the high plateaus of the Andes. In contrast to other members of its family, the plant has not spread beyond this region.

It was a basic food source for the Incas. Competition came when the Spanish tried to replace it with **barley**, but the experiment was unsuccessful as the climate of the high plateau turned out to be too harsh for the European grain. **Quinoa** is still consumed today in Latin America and the United States where it is highly prized, and recently it has even been introduced to Europe.

It has an upright, poorly branched-out trunk and alternate, long-stalked, very lobed, triangular, pointed leaves. The small simple flowers appear in terminal clusters around the stem. The monospermous fruit resemble small nuts. Today more resistant and more productive new varieties which do not contain saponine are cultivated, thus removing the necessity to soak the grains.

Quinoa is sown in the spring. Shortly before the grains have reached full maturity, about five months later, they can be harvested. If done later, the seeds would fall to the ground as the stalks were cut. The stalks are first left to dry, then they are threshed. Finally, the grain are removed from the husks as are other impurities. The leaves, which are eaten like **spinach**, can be harvested throughout the entire growth period while they are still young and green.

The grains contain much carbohydrate and protein, small amounts of lipids, cellulose and minerals salts like calcium, phosphorus and potassium. The leaves contain a lot of cellulose, proteins and sugar as well as minerals salts and vitamin C, and helps improve digestion.

Quinoa grains are a rich and nutritious food source which, as part of the daily diet helps prevent rickets. **Quinoa** flour mixed with **wheat** is used to make pastries, biscuits, crepes, porridges and soups. The fermented grains are used to prepare an alcoholic drink known as chicha, very popular among the Indian population. The leaves cooked in boiling water and seasoned are served with butter as an accompaniment to meat dishes. They are also used to make herbal pâtés, omelettes and stuffings. In agriculture, the leaves are also used as fodder.

CICHORIUM ENDIVIA   **Endive**
Leaf vegetable
Family: *Compositae*
Origin: *Western and Central Europe*
Height: *4 to 8 inches (10 to 20 cm)*
Flowering: *summer (from the second year)*
Properties: *apéritif, purifier, diuretic, stomachic, tonic*

The Greeks and Romans used **endives** for both their pharmacological and their culinary properties.

However, tastes have changed with time and **endives** are nowadays only prized by those amateurs who prefer crisp salads with a bitter flavor. This tendency has been emphasized by those producers who concentrate on the cultivation of other types of lettuce.

This biennial plant produces rosettes of leaves without forming heads. The foliage is dense, refreshing and delicately bitter. The green, more or less large leaves have white borders and are gathered together at the neck of the root. Its many varieties form two groups, the curly, or narrow leaf, and the Batavian, or broad leaf, **endive**. The small whitish flowers stand in panicles and bear achenes with a small, silky crown.

Endive thrives in loamy soil; the sowing takes place on a well prepared field which must be regularly watered during the whole growth period. When the required size has been reached, the heart is covered with plastic film which has the effect of reducing the bitterness, producing a milder and more tender lettuce. The same results can be achieved by placing the roots in glass containers. Because **endives** do not keep for long, they must be used right after being harvested. They are very rich in vitamin A and C and contain vitamin B, cellulose, a few carbohydrates, and bitter substances. They have diuretic and purifying properties. Prepared in salads, they form part of a well balanced diet. **Endives** stimulate the appetite and aid digestion and the elimination of toxins. They also stimulate and tonify the organism.

Endive salads

Endive can be eaten raw. A delicious salad can be made by adding diced bacon, garlic or finely grated Gruyere cheese. The leaves can also be prepared in the same manner as with a green vegetable. They can be boiled in salted water and sautéed in butter. They are also good when braised with cream, and are suitable for use in gratins, fritters, vegetable pies and soufflés.

CICHORIUM INTYBUS   **Chicory**
Leaf and Root vegetable
Family: *Compositae*
Origin: *Western and Central Europe*
Height: *12 to 56 inches (30 to 90 cm)*
Flowering: *from July to September (wild Chicoree); other varieties after the second summer*
Properties: *apéritif, laxative, diuretic, purifier, stomachic, tonic*

Chicory was mentioned as long as 4,000 years ago in the Ebers papyrus, an Egyptian compilation of medical texts and one of the oldest known to date. It was known to the Romans and eaten by them as a vegetable or in salads. **Chicory** is still prized today for its culinary and medicinal properties.

This perennial plant, which has been cultivated since the 17th century, has a rigid, branching, hairy stem. Its long, brown, fleshy taproot contains a white latex resin. The basal leaves are divided while the superior ones are lobed, elongated and toothed. The shining blue flowers of several petals appear in big terminal clusters and bear simple achenes.

Chicory is sown in July. Leaves are harvested from the following July up until the flowering starts, while the roots are harvested in the autumn.

Wild chicory has given way to a number of different varieties: **witloof** and **carla chicory**, **barbe de capucin**, **red chicory** from Vérone, **trévise chicory**, **sugarbread chicory**, and a number of other hybrids. **Witloof chicory** is a variety whose white leaves stand together so closely that it looks almost like a spindle. When exposed to direct light, **chicory** turns green and becomes even more bitter. The **carla** variety has red-rimmed leaves and is sweeter. **Chicory** is juicy, refreshing and crisp. It is grown from seed in the open in the spring. In autumn, the roots are dug out, and after the leaves are cut back to less than an inch (2 cm) from the neck they are stored over the winter in the cellar. From December to March the roots are stored in the darkness of the cellar, two thirds covered with damp sand at about 57–68 °F (14–20 °C).

Harvesting is done by hand three weeks later by cutting the lettuce head at the base of the leaves. The **barbe de capucin** variety is sown in July. Its long, blanched, green to pale yellow, loose leaves have a very indented stem. The leaves are soft, sweet, juicy and refreshing. Harvesting is also done by cutting the leaves less than an inch (2 cm) from the neck. The **red chicory** of **Vérone**, the **trévise**, and the **sugarbread** varieties form a type of head. **Red** and **trévise chicory** are crisp, with large white leaves and red stalks. Their flavor is less bitter and more pleasant. **Sugarbread chicory** has a moderately tight foliage with a long and wide green stem. It has a slightly bitter taste and is a great appetite stimulant. These varieties are generally sown in July in the open and are later thinned out and replanted 12 inches (30 cm) apart from each another. **Chicory** can withstand temperatures down to 18 °F (–8 °C). After the first head has been harvested, the stem can produce new heads to take its place.

Chicory contains a lot of water, cellulose, fiber, vitamin A (carotene), vitamins B, C and K, mineral salts (calcium, magnesium and phosphorus), amino acids, inulase as well as bitter substances. **Chicory** stimulates both the appetite and the digestion. It adjusts the metabolism, thereby detoxifying the organism. Because it is so rich in vitamins it is used in spring diets, and curative diets to cleanse the organism.

COLOCASIA ESCULENTA	**Taro or Eddo**
Root and leaf vegetable	
Family: Araceae	
Origin: Burma, tropical Asia	
Height: 24 to 28 inches (60 to 70 cm)	
Flowering: summer (seldom)	
Properties: nutritious, mineralizing, stimulant	

Taro is a very old plant which was already being cultivated in China about 2,000 years ago. Today there are approximately 1,000 different cultivated varieties worldwide, growing on damp as well as on dry soil. Taro can therefore be grown in Asian floodlands, on the Amazon delta, and in the relevant agricultural areas of Australia, Africa and India. In India it is known as **eddo**; in Hawaii, where it is consumed cooked, mashed and fermented, it is known as *poi*.

This plant with its creeping rhizome produces, depending on the variety, one large or several smaller edible tubers. It has very long stalks which carry oval or pointed leaves that tend to hang loosely when mature. Some species may have leaves as large as 20 inches (60 cm) in length and from 24 to 28 inches (60 to 70 cm) in width. The flowers, surrounded by a white spathe, appear deep between the leaf stalks, and bear very small shining berries. **Taro** is cultivated in hot climate zones. The tubers are planted in the spring in a well prepared, always damp soil. In Asia, the dachine and macabo varieties are widely cultivated. The tubers, which are harvested in late autumn, can only be stored for a short period of time because they perish quickly. For this reason there are numerous early and a late varieties, to ensure that fresh **taro** is readily available throughout the year.

Taro contains a lot of carbohydrate, carotene, vitamins B and C, as well as mineral salts such as calcium and magnesium. In the raw state, **taro** leaves, tubers and stems contain calcium oxalate which can cause severe skin irritation; they must therefore always be cooked, as heating destroys the irritant concerned. Nevertheless, it is a very nourishing and healthy vegetable. The tubers are cooked and served in salads, purees, as fritters, or sliced and sautéed in oil. The leaves and leaflets provide a very nourishing leaf vegetable which is a good accompaniment for meat and fish dishes. **Taro** tubers can be germinated in a glass of water, thus obtaining a very decorative tropical plant.

COPERNICIA MACROGLOSSA	**Caranuba wax palm**
Leaf and Stem vegetable	
Family: Coryphoideae	
Origin: northeast Brazil	
Height: 13 to 16.4 feet (4 to 5 m)	
Flowering: spring	
Properties: purifier, invigorating, stimulant, tonic	

This **wax palm** tree is named after the Carnaubeira indians who inhabit the area where the palm grows. This tree is very important for the economy of the region, providing the native population with numerous products such as wax, palm **cabbages**, sago, syrup and timber. The roofs of their huts are thatched with palm leaves, which also supplies the material for their hammocks. It is a small palm whose fanlike leaves appear in a spherical crown. Its trunk, which reaches

Taro

These tubers can be cooked and used in various salads, purees or fritters. They can be sliced and sautéed in hot oil. The leaves and the leaflets provide a highly prized green vegetable used to accompany a variety of meat and fish dishes.

only a diameter of about 8 inches (20 cm), is surrounded by a velvety mat of dead leaves that, with increasing age, cover only the top part of the tree leaving behind numerous stigmata on the rest of the trunk. The tree has approximately fifteen splendid greenish-blue leaves, which spread out, on a span of about 7 feet (2 m), approximately sixty fanned segments each of about 5 feet (1.50 m) in length. The small hermaphrodite flowers appear in ramified inflorescences and bear green, egg-shaped fruit.

This variety of palm tree is quite useful; it produces vegetable, edible substances which are rich in sugar, starch and mineral salts. The leaf buds are consumed as a vegetable similar to palm hearts. After the woody fibers of the trunk have been rinsed several times, sago, a very nutritious food starch is extracted. A sugar syrup is obtained from the juice of the trunk which is used to make an alcoholic beverage known as Arrak. And finally, this decorative palm tree is a welcome addition to any tropical garden.

CRAMBE MARITIMA　　　　　　**Sea kale**
Leaf vegetable
Family: Cruciferae
Origin: north and west coasts of Europe
Height: 12 inches (30 cm)
Flowering: May to July
Properties: purifier, diuretic, anti-scurvy, antiseptic

Sea kale is a shrub which loves salty soil; therefore, it is to be found on the seashores and cliffs of both the Mediterranean Sea and the Atlantic Ocean. **Sea kale,** the taste of which resembles **cabbage,** has been around for quite a time. That renowned vegetable expert **Louis XIV** knew of it, and ordered its cultivation in the gardens of Versailles. The plant has a thick, woody, pale green trunk with large, bluish-green, fleshy, lobed, waxy, coarsely toothed leaves. Honey fragrant, clustered sprays of white, four petaled flowers rise from the basal leaves. They bear small, round, split fruit containing the seeds. **Sea kale** thrives in cool, deep and salty soil and a sunny location in mild, damp climate zones. It's cultivated from seed directly onto the field from March to June, through division of shoots in the spring, or through division of the root into pieces of 4 inches (10 cm) long with at least two buds. The young, fleshy, white shoots with pink leaf buds are harvested. The young, external

leaves are also edible; however, to ensure they lose their bitter taste they should be blanched before hand. When harvesting the leaves, care should be taken not to damage the heart of the plant which can remain for several years. **Sea kale** perishes quickly, so it should be consumed immediately. However, the blanched leaves can be frozen or preserved. **Sea kale** is rich in vitamin C, mineral salts, sulphur and iodine. It has a metabolism-stimulating effect, thereby detoxifying the organism. Because of its high vitamin C content, it is used to prevent scurvy as well as viral infections.

Blanched in boiling water, the sprouts may be served as an entrée with a vinaigrette or mayonnaise. It is also delicious when coated in meat juices, covered in béchamel sauce, baked in the oven and served as a side dish with meat.

CUCUMIS SATIVUS　　　　**Cucumber and Gherkin**
Fruit vegetable
Family: Cucurbitaceae
Origin: probably western Asia
Height: About 8 feet (2.50 m)
Flowering: May to July
Properties: diuretic, emollient, refreshing, tonic

This annual, creeping plant is widely cultivated in temperate regions for its fruit. **Cucumbers** have a rough, succulent, trailing stem which bears branched tendrils by which the plant can be trained to supports. Its hairy, very serrated leaves have three to five pointed lobes and a conspicuous palmate vein on their edges. The trumpet-shaped yellow flowers are unisexual because they can sometimes be male (five stamens on three entities) and sometimes female. Fertilization occurs through self-pollination, but not necessarily through cross-pollination. **Cucumbers** cultivated in greenhouses only bear fruit through parthenogenesis. The more or less large fruit are very succulent, elongated berries. According to the species the skin is green, yellow or white, bright and smooth or covered with spines. Their flesh is crisp, light green and enclosing manyl seeds arranged in six rows.

Raw **cucumbers** have an insipid, watery, sometimes bitter taste. Gardeners have managed to create less bitter hybrids by eliminating cucurbitacin C, the substance responsible for such bitterness.

Cucumber

Raw cucumbers make a refreshing salad or appetizer simply sprinkled with lemon juice and olive oil, or with a creamy dressing of yogurt, cream cheese and herbs. Cooked it is used as a side dish accompanying meat, fowl, fish and mussels. It can also be chopped or cut lengthwise, removing the seeds and stuffing it with rice, olives, minced meat or fish – seasoned with a pinch of garlic – and then baked in the oven. In England it is used to prepare a soup. Mashed, seasoned with green aniseed and chilled, it is a delicious accompaniment for cold cuts. Small cucumbers can be pickled. After rubbing them thoroughly with a dry cloth, they are marinated in either brine or vinegar and herbs. Larger cucumbers can be cut and preserved in the same way.

Gherkins are small immature **cucumbers** which are regularly used in pickles. Some varieties are the "small green of Paris," short, crisp and very thorny; the large **gherkin** of "Massy," and the "Kerby," which has an intense green color and is picked when it is very young. **Cucumbers** are extensively grown in frames or on trellises in greenhouses; in milder climates they are cultivated as a field crop and in home gardens in moist, well drained soil sheltered from humidity and cold. An excess of seed is sown in March or April, and the seedlings are thinned out to the number desired in May. The shoots are pinched off and when the stems appear, three or four leaves are picked off, leaving a leaf on top of the fruit. **Gherkins** are cultivated in the same way, but they are not pinched.

Even though **cucumbers** contain a lot of water, they are not diuretic. They contain magnesium which promotes growth and the development of bones, iodine, and trace elements necessary for hormonal and cellular metabolism. **Cucumbers** are used to soothe the skin, eliminate blotchy complexions, freckles and wrinkles.

Pumpkin and Squash

For pumpkins and squash there are numerous recipies, according to which they may be used for sweet or savory dishes. They can be cooked with onions in purees, gratins or in soups. Cut into pieces, cooked in the pressure cooker and seasoned with parsley and garlic they are served as a vegetable to accompany meat dishes. Sweet, they are used to make pies and vanilla desserts. They can be used to prepare souf-flés, added to pancake batter, and pureed as a side dish. They are also used to make rissoles, brioche, and ice cream. Raw and cut into pieces they are served as an hors-d'œuvre, and grated they are added to salads with lemon-juice, raisins and roasted almonds. The seeds are boiled or roasted. They are rich in amino acids and proteins. Spaghetti pumpkin is cooked in boiling water until the fibers in its flesh take on the consistency of noodles. This vegetable spaghetti is used as a garnish for meat dishes or served as a main dish with cheese, ham and basil. Because of their different colors and shapes, pumpkins are also used as a household decoration.

CUCURBITA MAXIMA	Winter squash or Pumpkin

Fruit vegetable
Family: *Cucurbitaceae*
Origin: *North and South America*
Height: *10 to 13 feet (3 to 4 m)*
Flowering: *May to July*
Properties: *soothing, tranquilizer, laxative, vermifuge (seeds)*

The original cultivators of the **Winter squash**, the largest most popular variety of **pumpkin** due to its characteristic form and color, were the American Indians. The European colonists considered it at first to be an oversized melon; whereas, centuries later, the jack-o-lanterns with their grotesque grinning faces, first cut by Irish immigrants to North America, have become the epitome of Halloween.

On All Saints' Eve, children dressed up as ghosts, witches, demons, monsters and other such scary beings go from door to door collecting sweets – but always with the threat that if refused, they will play a trick on the householder (trick or treat).

It is an annual plant that climbs by a simple, sometimes branched, spirally coiled tendril. It has long stalked, palmate, velvety and soft leaves that alternate

along the stem. Most species have unisexual flowers, which are borne in the leaf axils and have five white or yellow petals; male flowers have five anthers, and female flowers have five carpels. The fruit in most species is a fleshy, round, many-seeded berry with a tough rind, often attaining considerable size and growing close to the ground. It can weigh, according to the species, between 6 and 110 lbs. (3 and 50 kg).

Pumpkins generally have a smooth and usually lightly furrowed or ribbed shell with a thick, sweet flesh and a large amount of edible seeds. Among the favorite **pumpkin** varieties are: red **pumpkin of Etampes**, a scalloped and flattened fruit with strikingly red flesh; the great yellow of Paris, a big fruit with a thick, yellow flesh; the **Alençon pumpkin** with its oblong shaped, ribbed and shinny fruit which can weigh up to 44 lbs.

(20 kg); the **golden hubbard**, an orange, woody variety with a sweet, fine, compact and very aromatic flesh. There is also the **autumn queen pumpkin** which can weigh up to 33 lbs. (15 kg) and which has an elongated, round shape with a dark green shell and a pinkish yellow flesh that is quite mediocre. The most well known **pumpkin** is the **turban pumpkin** with its decorative orange, green, yellow and red fruit weighing from

6 to 9 lbs. (3 to 4 kg). It has a high quality floury, sweet flesh. There is also the "**Giraumon Galeux d'Eysines**" **pumpkin** weighing about 4.4 lbs. (2 kg) with a thin pink shell which is covered with small excrescencies when ripe. The **Hokkaido pumpkin** has a delicate orange flesh and is rich in vitamins, mineral salts, amino acids, fatty acids, fiber, sugar and carotene. Its taste is similar to that of chestnuts. Its shape and color vary according to variety: the "**chestnut bush**" has a grey blue, tasty flesh; the 8.8 lbs. (4 kg) "**golden delicious**" is yellow with an orange flesh and very rich in vitamins; the "**kabocha**" is a medium-sized, spherical, dark green **pumpkin** with bright orange, sweet, starchy flesh used in soups or roasted. "**Delicata**" and "**sweet dumpling**" **pumpkins** have green striped fruits with an exceptionally sweet, orange flesh whose taste is similar to that of chestnuts. The "nice" variety has a firm pulp that is extremely delicious; and the "**spaghetti pumpkin,**" native to Manchuria, has oblong fruit the delicate flesh of which has long fibers that are highly digestive and light. Finally, there are a few dwarf varieties like the "**sugar pie**" **pumpkin** whose very sweet flesh is used to make **pumpkin pie**; and the "**pepper**" and "**gland**" **pumpkins** whose flesh is sweet and nutty.

    Pumpkin is enjoyed in both sweet and savory dishes; as a puree, a gratin, fritters or in soups. It makes an excellent vegetable side dish when diced, steamed, and then seasoned with garlic and parsley. It is suitable for many sweet dishes, ranging from cakes to jam. The **dwarf pumpkin** is used in soups, chestnut soufflés and as a puree for meat dishes, but also in biscuits and desserts. Pumpkins are also prized for their decorative value in the household, whether it be for Thanksgiving or for Halloween, or simply as charming piece of natural decoration. The decorative properties of the **pumpkin** in the garden is not to be overlooked, whether it be the large-leafed plant with its pretty yellow flowers, or the ripe colored fruit that provide attraction.

Moschata pumpkin

Nutmeg and butternut pumpkins are used as ingredients for cakes, pies and soufflés as well as aromatic soups served with cream. They are also used to prepare warm or cold sweets, desserts flavored with vanilla, cinnamon or chocolate. Other varieties are used in purees, fritters, and vegetable gratins. The roasted, salted seeds are served as a snack with apéritifs.

CUCURBITA MOSCHATA   *Moschata pumpkin*

Fruit vegetable
Family: *Cucurbitaceae*
Origin: *North and Central America*
Height: *10 to 13 feet (3 to 4 m)*
Flowering: *June to July*
Properties: *soothing, laxative, nutritious, vermifuge (seeds)*

The **moschata pumpkin** differs from the other plants of the *Cucurbita* type by its very short calyx and its soft leaves. It often bears only a single, firm-fleshy fruit. The **moschata pumpkin** is generally medium sized, except for the **portemanteau** variety cultivated in Italy whose fruit can reach up to 3 feet (1 m) in length and weigh 44 lbs. (20 kg). Even though, the **moschata pumpkin** has the same characteristic features and quali-

ties of other **pumpkins**. The most popular varieties are the "**sucrine**" and "**butternut**" **pumpkins** due to their sweet flavor. The "**trompe d'Albanga**" stands out because of its long, twisted shape. Like most **pumpkins**, the **moschata pumpkin** also needs rich, well drained soil and plenty of sun. The fruits are harvested when they are ripe – usually in autumn. Stored dry, they keep fresh for three to six months.

CUCURBITA PEPO   *Zucchini, Courgette, Gourd, Summer squash*

Fruit vegetable
Family: Cucurbitaceae
Origin: Central America
Height: 10 to 13 feet (3 to 4 m)
Flowering: May to July
Properties: soothing, laxative, mineralizing, sedative, vermifuge

Popular among the natives of Central America, the *Curcubita pepo* arrived in Europe during the 16th century. Today, they are prized in the United States and Eastern and Southern Europe alike. This perennial plant differs in its appearance according to the variety: some have long, trailing stems and others have short hairy ones. The large, more or less lobed leaves have a long, spiny leaf stalk. The orange flowers can reach a diameter of up to 6 inches (15 cm); they bear more numerous and smaller fruit than those of the *Cucurbita maxima* variety. The elongated, green **zucchini**, also known as **courgette**, which has a white juicy flesh, is attached to the stem by a short and angular peduncle. **Gourds** are mostly round. **Summer squash** have a flesh similar to that of the **artichoke**; flat and round, they have scalloped, smooth, ridged, or warty surfaces with ten horn-like outgrowths and a white, yellow, star shaped flesh. All of these **pumpkins** contain in their thick flesh numerous seeds that are small and soft when young, and hard when mature.

The rind which is often smooth becomes hard with age. **Zucchini** and **summer squash** can be eaten with their skin, but they must be harvested before they are ripe. **Gourds,** which are usually peeled before being prepared, are harvested when they are ripe. The following are some of the most popular **gourds** worth mentioning: the **acceste**, the **aurore**, the **tamarino**, the **d'Altai-Kaja**, and the **nice** variety with its aniseed taste and without a doubt the most succulent one of all. Finally, there is, of course, the **spaghetti gourd** which has a white flesh whose fibers resemble noodles. These fruit contain a lot of water, a few lipids, and sugar; therefore, they are not very nutritious. Nevertheless, they are healthy, easy to digest, and recommended in diets designed to lose weight. They contain a lot of vitamin C, vitamin A, and trace elements.

Cultivation is done from seed. The plants require a rich soil, plenty of sun and a lot of water. The plant responds badly to dryness, so care must be taken to ensure it is well watered. The harvest begins in July which allows the growth of another generation of fruit. Because the **courgettes** are harvested before maturity, they are highly perishable, however, they can be blanched and frozen.

As most of the fruit have a rather watery taste they should be prepared with care. They are generally eaten in purees and soups seasoned with garlic, thyme or mint. Sliced or cut in cubes and sautéed with garlic and parsley, they are a delicate accompaniment to meat dishes. Stuffed or in a gratin, these vegetables can be served as a main dish. Peeled and without seeds, **summer squash** can be cooked in boiling salted water, seasoned and served warm or cold in a vinaigrette or with mayonnaise.

CYNARA CARDUNCULUS — Cardoon

Stem vegetable
Family: Compositae
Origin: Central Europe, North Africa
Height: about 3 feet (1 m)
Flowering: early summer
Properties: rich in inulin (a sugar substitute for diabetics), apéritif, laxative, diuretic, tonic

---

This thistle-like vegetable, closely related to the **artichoke**, has a great chard with long, fleshy stalks. There are two types: the original, very prickly wild form and the vegetable **cardoon**, a new variety without prickles. The **wild cardoon** has been used since ancient times in the kitchens of North Africa and northern Egypt. Once forgotten, it has become fashionable once more thanks to those great chefs who fell in love with its fine, delicate taste. Today, it is a very popular vegetable. The variety without prickles is cultivated mostly in the southeastern part of France.

This biennial, fast growing shrub is however, generally cultivated annually. It has a milky, bitter sap and big, long-stalked, lobed, thick, and fleshy leaves. The wild varieties have prickly leaves, which the newer cultivated varieties do not have. Contrary to the popular saying "there's no good **cardoon** without prickles," these latter ones are quite tasty and tender. The purple flowers appear during the second year on long stems reaching about 4 feet (1.20 m).

The most famous popular varieties are the **thornless simple white**, the **Tours** or **Spanish cardoon** which is very thorny, and the "red-stemmed" **cardoon**. **Cardoon** thrives in sunny locations and require a deep and moist soil. It is sown in May. Once the seedlings are strong enough, they are replanted at about 1 yard (1 m) intervals to give them enough room to grow. Three weeks before the harvest, which can take place according to demand from August up to the beginning of the winter frosts, the **cardoons** are blanched, to reduce their bitter taste, make them sweeter and tender.

Cardoon

Cardoons, like celery, are peeled in order to remove the fibrous threads. Immediately after that, they are rubbed with lemon juice, to prevent their discoloring. They are then cooked for two hours in boiling water in which previously a little bit of flour was added. Prepared in this way, they can be served with butter, meat juices, or sprinkled with chopped herbs to accompany white meat. They can also be fried and used in gratins.

In order to do this, the leaves are tied together or they are covered with cardboard or black plastic leaving the tips of the plant exposed to the light so that it continues to grow. Earth is also banked up around the roots. Harvesting is done by cutting the leaves at the base of the stem or pulling out the seedlings with the sod. These are then stored in the dark with the leaves tied together. In this way they keep fresh the whole winter long.

If the winter is not too rough (**cardoons** are not hardy), the seedlings can remain outside, well protected from the cold. **Cardoons** are rich in inulin, a sugar substitute for diabetics. Due to their high mucilage content, they are laxative and refreshing. They also contain mineral salts and carbohydrates.

CYNARA SCOLYMUS — Artichoke

Flower vegetable
Family: Compositae
Origin: Mediterranean region
Height: 4 to 4.5 feet (1.20 to 1.40 m)
Flowering: late spring (every two years)
Properties: apéritif, laxative, purifier, diuretic, tonic

Artichoke

Young artichokes can be eaten raw with salt, paprika sauce or in a salad. After cutting the stems back from where they join the fruit and breaking off the very tough leaves, the artichokes are marinated in lemon juice and olive oil. Cooked artichokes must be rapidly consumed because they develop toxins that can cause digestion problems. To prepare artichoke hearts, they should be carefully washed, cut off down to where the heart begins while pulling out the spiny choke that lies on top of the heart, and cooked in boiling salted water. Upon cooling they are served with a vinaigrette or mayonnaise as an hors-d'œuvre or main dish. They can also be stuffed with vegetables or meat and cooked in the oven. Artichokes can also be quartered and cooked with stock or parsley and garlic. They can be prepared in a gratin with béchamel sauce and grated cheese, or simply in an omelette. In Italy, artichokes are used to produce an apéritif.

It is believed that **artichokes** originated in Ethiopia from where they spread to Egypt and the rest of the world. Today they are cultivated all over Europe. Unknown in the wild, it is likely that they are descended from the **cardoon** which is the single known wild form of this type of vegetable. Not until the Renaissance, after numerous breeding attempts, did the **artichoke** appear in the kitchen gardens of southern Europe. Even though at the time it was already clearly different from the **cardoon**, it was developed further during the following centuries becoming the **artichoke** known to us today. Nowadays it is extensively cultivated in California, France, Belgium, and the Mediterranean countries. The **artichoke** is a large, coarse, herbaceous, thistle-like perennial plant with a big, closed and fibrous root full of radicles. The deeply cut, large, woolly leaves are white on the top, whitish on the underside and appear in loose rosettes. During the second year, sturdy, branched flower stalks rise giving way to purplish flowers which are formed by a big calyx with fleshy, pointed scales that cover one another. Inside they are covered by silky, hairy, oval seeds. The seeds ripen in September and are very popular among birds. During the flowering, these flowers are very decorative.

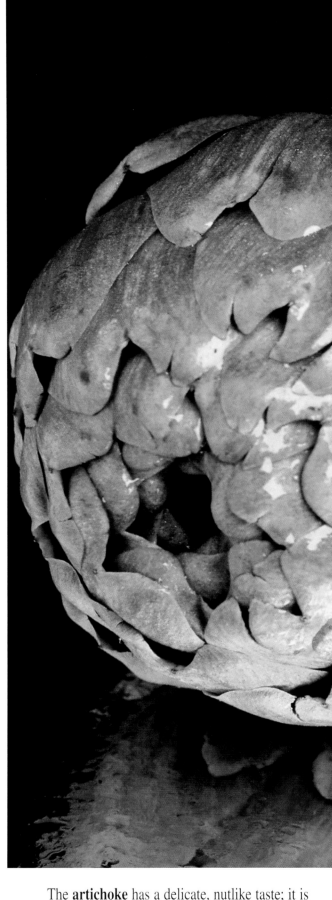

The **artichoke** has a delicate, nutlike taste; it is starchy and at the same time sweet and slightly bitter. It needs light, deep, airy, acid soil rich in humus, and a warm sunny location. The French varieties are a little bit more resistant than the more demanding Italian ones. The **artichoke** is planted in the spring, by planting divisions of the crown or rooted offshoots. It can also be propagated by sowing, but it tends to degenerate.

Harvesting is done before it blooms, once the heart has reached its full size, approximately 3 to 4 inches (8 to 10 cm) in diameter. The parts of the plant above ground are cut back before winter and it is covered with hay or soil. After four years, the plants are no longer harvested because they begin to degenerate. It is a healthy vegetable, rich in vitamins B and C and containing mineral salts and inulin, a substitute sugar for diabetics.

CYPERUS ESCULENTUS   **Earth almond or Chufa**

Root vegetable
Family: Cyperaceae
Origin: southern Europe, Asia and North Africa
Height: 8 to 24 inches (20 to 60 cm)
Flowering: summer
Properties: soothing, hypotensive, laxative, nutritious

The **earth almond** is to be found wild in the basin of the White Nile, in Upper Egypt and the Sudan. Its cultivation was known in Ancient Egypt, as tubers have been found in the graves of Pharaohs from the 2nd and 3rd millennia BC. **Theophrastus** acknowledged it as an edible plant, to be found growing on the banks of rivers, the tuber of which could be cooked in beer.

Earth almond is cultivated mostly as an oil plant. Its oil is comparable in quality to olive oil and is used extensively by the food industry. For this reason a variety of bigger tubers providing greater yields has been developed. This hardy shrub has leaves with parallel veins. Its straw colored terminal flowers bear shinny reddish-brown seeds.

In Europe, **earth almond** rarely blooms. It is propagated through its reddish, oval or globular tubers which appear by the thousands at the end of the short rhizome of any given bush. The plant thrives in sandy, damp soil with plenty of sun. The tubers are planted in April and harvested in October by pulling the whole plant from the earth. The tubers are collected and washed. Containing about 20% oil, **earth almonds** produce a high quality edible oil which is used to fight against cardio-vascular diseases. In addition, it contains 30% fiber, 15% carbohydrates and up to 10% protein, as well as vitamins A and B. These tubers are quite nutritious.

The oil with its almond like taste is used to season salads and to roast meat and fish. The tubers themselves are consumed like **almonds,** fresh or dried, but can also be roasted like peanuts. From the roasted tubers, a flour is obtained which can be used to make pastries and cakes. It is also used to prepare a hot drink similar to cocoa. Cooked in salted water, the tubers are a tasty vegetable accompaniment for meat, fowl, rabbit and lamb. They are also deliciously nutritious when prepared as a puree or in soups. The raw tubers are used as fodder for pigs.

The **carrot** is known throughout Europe, growing on the pathside and in meadows. The distant ancestor of the **carrot** was a wild species to be found in Eurasia, and when humans first discovered it, the root was white. For some unknown reason a new variety with an orangey-yellow root spontaneously developed in Afghanistan.

The **carrot** is a biennial plant that produces an edible fleshy taproot. The root is generally white or orange and bears an erect rosette of doubly compound, finely divided leaves above ground. During the second year, large, branched flower stalks arise. They are hollow, have a circular cross section and can reach up to more than 30 inches (80 cm) high. The ends of the main stalk and branches bear large compound umbels of tiny white flowers formed by approximately 20 rays in the center of which a sterile, dark purple flower is formed. The flowers bear small elongated, oval, dented, spiny seeds. **Carrots** have a characteristic sweet, herbal fragrance; their taste is soft, sweet, and slightly bitter. **Carrot** is grown from seed at the end of March directly onto the field, and harvested three months later. Late varieties are sown from the end of May to mid-June and harvested six months later. Once the seeds have germinated, the plants are thinned out at intervals of a little more than an inch (3 cm) apart from each other. The tiny **carrots** seen during this procedure can already be eaten. **Carrots** can be harvested upon demand during the whole season. Autumn **carrots** keep longer if they are left two to three days to dry in the sun.

Carrots are rich in beta carotine which the body transforms into vitamin A, an essential vitamin for the development of children. It supports the intake of minerals and the regeneration of the skin by stimulating melanin production and facilitating the absorption of proteins. It also helps prevent night blindness and improves vision. **Carrots** contain B vitamins, a lot of vitamin C, as well as vitamins D and E. Moreover, they supply the body with trace elements and amino acids.

Carrot

These attractively colored roots are eaten both in a raw and a cooked state. Raw and grated with some lemon juice and olive oil, they render a delicious, refreshing hors-d'œuvre. The juice is useful against spring tiredness. Steamed or cooked in salted water, they are served tossed in meat juices or butter as an accompaniment to other dishes. They taste delicious prepared with cream, and are a traditional combination with peas. Carrot puree goes well with white meats such as roast veal. They are used as an ingredient for soufflés and sweet and savory pies. Sliced, they can be sautéed in butter with parsley and garlic. Carrots are a very healthy and easy to digest vegetable. Their popularity is due to the fact that they are easy to prepare in a variety of different ways.

DAUCUS CAROTA   **Carrot**
Root vegetable
Family: *Umbelliferae*
Origin: *Eurasia*
Height: *8 to 12 inches (20 to 30 cm)*
Flowering: *summer (from the second year)*
Properties: *soothing, anti-anaemia, improves vision, laxative, mineralizing, regenerates tissue*

DIOSCOREA   **Yam**
Root vegetable
Family: *Dioscoreaceae*
Origin: *all tropical regions of the world*
Height: *according to sort 6 to 10 feet (2 to 3 m)*
Flowering: *spring (inconspicuously)*
Properties: *nutritious, purgative, stimulant, tonic*

Worldwide there are at least forty different varieties of **yam** whose tubers serve as food and animal fodder. They are an important agricultural commodity in Africa, especially in Cameroon and Togo where they are part of the everyday diet. They were successfully introduced in France in 1853 by **Monsieur de Montigny**. Today **yams** are cultivated in the Loire valley and consumed mainly by people of Asian, African and South American origin living in Paris. The world's biggest **yam** producer is Nigeria, followed by the Ivory Coast and Brazil.

The plant is a woody vine with thick tubers from which protrude long, slender, annual, climbing stems which are reinforced with a sort of hook. The alternate or opposite leaves are either entire or lobed. The greenish white and very fragrant flowers, generally small and individually inconspicuous, though collectively showy, appear in clusters on the leaf axils. They bear three-celled, three-winged dry berries containing an ovary which when ripe liberates numerous flat seeds. The underground taproot carries several black or purple edible tubers which can reach magnificent sizes.

Dioscorea alata and *rotundata* are the most widely cultivated white **yam** varieties. Native to West Africa, they are highly tolerant of long dry seasons. The *Dioscorea batatas* is an Asian **yam** with white or reddish flesh whose tubers can measure up to a yard (1 m) in length and weigh 44 lbs. (20 kg). Globular tubers of *Dioscorea globosa* variety also have a white flesh and a very sweet taste. They are cultivated predominantly in India. Finally, there are the *Dioscorea esculenta* and *bulbifera* varieties which form large tubers on the leaf axils and which can also withstand periods of drought.

The cultivation of **yams** is relatively easy provided the climate is warm and humid. The tubers are planted, like **potatoes**, in loose earth with good drainage. They are harvested approximately ten months later. All **yam** varieties are rich in fiber and starch. There are also a few that contain dioscorin, a toxic alkaloid which dissipates with cooking. Furthermore, they supply vitamins B and C, as well as different minerals.

Yams are a very nutritious vegetable which tonify the organism. Before being cooked, they must be washed with plenty of water, in order to reduce the dioscorin content as much as possible. They are cooked in boiling water and served as an accompaniment to meat and fish.

Palmetto

Once the exterior cover is removed, palmettos can be eaten either raw or cooked, and are a delicious addition to salads. They are crisp and tender with a slight nutty taste, and can also be sliced and added to other vegetables or served as an accompaniment to sweet-savory dishes. In Brazil a creamy, brown beverage is prepared with the pulp obtained from pressing the fresh palmetto. Because palmettos do not keep for long, they are usually only found canned.

EUTERPE EDULIS — *Palm hearts, Palmetto*

Stem vegetable
Family: Arecaceae
Origin: tropical and subtropical regions
Height: about 131 feet (40 m)
Flowering: spring
Properties: purifier, mineralizing, tonic

Like most palm trees, the *Euterpe edulis* produces **palmettos**. This palm tree is an important source of food in tropical countries where it is also cultivated as an export product. Seeds were found on the coasts of Costa Rica which date from 2300 to 1700 BC.

This big palm tree of upright growth has a slim trunk with ring-shaped stigma left behind by dead leaves. It has a bright grey-green coloring. Its long leaves, 6 to 10 feet (2 to 3 m) long, are stalked and pinnate. They appear at the head of the trunk forming a hanging tuft. The leaf stalk flows into the central vein of the leaf which can have forty to eighty thin, pinnate, linear or lancelike leaflets. The flowers appear in groups of three (two male ones and one female). They have white sepals and dark-purple petals. The cone that grows at the very top of the tree is known as the **palm heart** or **palmetto**.

The cultivation and harvest of this plant are simple. When the fruit become ripe, the heart, or **palmetto**, is cut off. After this, the tree dies quickly leaving at its base some shoots from which a new tree will grow. These shoots can also be harvested; however, they are regularly left untouched in order to preserve the species.

Palmettos contain fibre, iron, magnesium, calcium, and lipids, but only a few carbohydrates. They are a healthy and nutritious vegetable. Because they contain trace elements, they help fight against anaemia and have a mineralizing effect on the organism.

FOENICULUM VULGARE — **Fennel**

Family: Umbelliferae
Origin: southern Europe, Asia Minor
Height: about 5 feet (1.50 m)
Flowering: June to August
Properties: antispasmodic, carminative, digestive, diuretic, expectorant, galactagogue, stimulant

Fennel is a vegetable with an inflated base or false bulb and an aniseed aroma developed by improving the basal leaves of aromatic **fennel**. During the 17th century the Italians transformed this aromatic plant into the fragrant, juicy vegetable highly prized nowadays.

The plant is quite small with a white, climbing taproot and an inflated bulb. The bulb which is compressed on the sides is formed by a petioled base wrapped around the stem. It forms a head that becomes round when ripe. The bluish-green leaves have a long stalk and are divided in thin, filiform straps which form a dense tuft emerging from the centre of the bulb. The hollow, branched stem, which appears during the second year, carries yellow, terminal flower umbels that bear fruit, or seeds, which are split in two thin and elongated achenes. The part of the plant that is consumed is the inflated base of the leaves. There are four main varieties: the "bologne," the "sicilie," the "palerme" whose large, round and short petioles are eaten raw, and the "florence" **fennel** whose elongated petioles are preferred for cooking. The plant thrives in warm, sunny regions in rich, moist and fertilized soil. It is sown directly onto the field from April to July. Once the shoots have developed, the plant is thinned out and the roots are covered with hay to keep them moist.

Fennel bulbs are highly perishable; therefore, it is better to consume them quickly. Nevertheless, they can be put in dark or cold storage. They will keep tender and juicy, if the shoot has been pulled out with a piece of the root and the external leaves have been cut off. This vegetable is low in calories, but is rich in anethole. It has an antispasmodic effect on the stomach and colon. Because it prevents intestinal fermentation, it is an excellent carminative and digestive. Its seeds stimulate the secretion of milk in women. It is rich in mineral salts, vitamins A, B, and C, water and fibre. It is very nutritional and refreshing for the organism. It is also believed to be an aid against impotence.

Fennel
The raw bulbs with their sweet, aniseed flavor, are delicious in simple or mixed salads. They can be cut in slices and served as an appetizer. Sautéed in butter or braised in stock, with cream or in a gratin they compliment meat and fish dishes. The seeds are used to make licorice while the leaves are used in salads or to give aroma to cold sauces. A decoction of the roots is used to help the organism eliminate toxins; therefore, it is recommended in weight loss diets.

GLYCERIA FLUITANS   *Riccia*
Fruit vegetable
Family: Gramineae
Origin: Europe, Morocco, North and South America
Height: 16 inches to over 3 feet (40 cm to 1 m)
Flowering: May to August
Properties: emollient, laxative, mineralizing, stimulant

Riccia is a strong herb which is found in the wild floating on the banks of ponds and rivers. In former times it was called "manna" and up until the 19th century, its nutritious seeds were sold on markets. In Poland, Silesia and East Prussia the plant was highly appreciated. In the 17th century it was cultivated in all free ponds and other damp areas. Today, this plant has been replaced by nobler cereals like **wheat**.

It is a hardy, aquatic, herbaceous plant with branching ribbons that carry narrow, bluish-green leaves. In the spring, a fine unilateral inflorescence, composed of pistils that will later produce fruit, appears at the top the stem. These fruit are elongated and yellow or white.

Their appearance and taste is similar to that of **wheat**. The superficial roots or ribbons often become tangled in large masses and cling to other vegetation floating in the water. **Riccia** prospers only on a soil which is always flooded with water. It is sown in the autumn or in winter. The successive harvest of the fruit, or caryopsis, begins in April and ends in October. They are gathered during rainy or foggy weather as the humidity prevents the fruit from drying up and setting free the seeds.

Riccia is a grain rich in starch, carbohydrates, amino acids, sugar and cellulose. It also contains lipids, potassium, phosphorus and calcium as well as B vitamins and vitamin E. It is a very healthy food which is used during convalescence and winter months. It promotes growth, prevents rickets and other diseases caused by mineral deficiency. It also helps calm the nervous system.

In the kitchen, the seeds are cooked in plain or aromatized milk to make cakes similar to those baked with **wheat**. Cooked in salted water, the seeds are served as a couscous-like accompaniment to meat and vegetables. Furthermore, they can also be used to thicken soups and stuffings. In agriculture its delicate and digestible hay is used as a cattle feed.

GLYCINE MAX	**Soy bean**

Fruit and stem vegetable
Family: *Fabaceae*
Origin: *Manchuria and Korea*
Height: *1.6 to 5 feet (0.50 to 1.50 m)*
Flowering: *spring*
Properties: *fights against fatigue, anti-cholesterol, energizing, nutritious, mineralizing*

Soy beans

Soy bean shoots are eaten raw, mostly with a vinaigrette, or also cooked as a vegetable ingredient of meat and fish dishes. They are a typical component of a lot of Far Eastern foods. The immature soy beans taste like young peas. The flour which is produced from the ripe seeds is used to prepare both sweet and savory breads and pastries. From the fermented seeds, soy milk is produced and used to make a type of cheese rich in iron and magnesium known as tofu. In the vegetarian kitchen, tofu is cut in pieces and added to other vegetables. The cooked beans can be mashed to a puree and used for both sweet and savory dishes. Soy beans are also used to produce tempe, a kind of "vegetarian meat" which is rich in vitamin B12 and calcium. It is prepared by mixing wheat flour with thick soy bean puree. This carefully kneaded dough is used to make flat pancakes that can be cooked like meat, fried in a pan or cut into pieces and added to ragouts and other braised dishes. Furthermore, soy beans produce an oil which is used mainly in the industrial production of paints, emulsions and soaps.

The **soy bean**, which is used to produce seasonings, as a vegetable, and as the source of an oil with many uses, has been cultivated in China and Japan since 3,000 BC, where it was classified as one of the five sacred crops. It was only in the 18th century however, that missionaries brought it to Europe, where it was grown at Kew Gardens for the first time. In the US, **soy beans** were introduced in the early 19th century. There, **soy** farming was expanded dramatically after World War II. **Soy beans** are one of the most widely consumed vegetables in the world.

It is a type of dwarf bean with stems that can reach up to 5 feet (1.50 m) high. Its root has numerous nodules containing bacteria known as rhizobium which have the ability to convert the nitrates in the soil into large amounts of nitrogen. The whole plant is covered with fine hairs and has odd-pinnate, lobed leaves. Its white, self-fertilizing flowers appear in clusters on the axils of the leaf and bear fruit or pods which contain three to six seeds.

The **soy bean** is grown from seed during the spring. It may be cultivated in most types of soil, but it thrives in warm, subtropical climates in humid, well drained, sandy loam. It requires at least fourteen hours of sunlight a day. Some of the beans can be harvested before they mature to be used as **peas**. However, they are really harvested when the beans are very ripe using a combine harvester. There is a greenhouse culture that is only for the production of shoots and **soy bean** sprouts.

Soy beans produce a flour rich in vegetable proteins (35 to 40%), lipids (20%), essential and saturated fat (85%), carbohydrates (36 to 38%), sucrose and raffinose. Furthermore, **soy beans** contain mineral salts, phosphorous, potassium, iron, calcium, and vitamins B and C.

It is a balancing vegetable. Its flour contains a lot of lecithin which is a natural lipid that acts as an emulsi-fier and helps the body dissolve fat in the blood. It also helps fight arteriosclerosis and reduces cholesterol levels due to its high levels of choline and inositol. Moreover, the phosphorous contained in the lecithin facilitates the functioning of the brain cells. Recently, isoflavones have been isolated form **soy bean** flour with estrogenic properties which can help fight against menopausal problems.

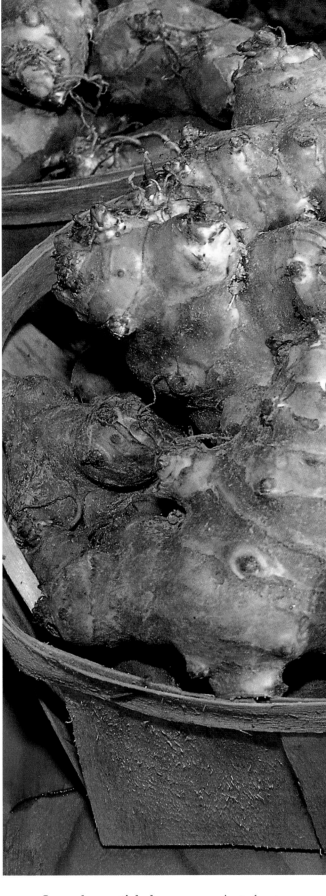

HELIANTHUS TUBEROSUS

Jerusalem artichoke

Root vegetable

Family: *Compositae*

Origin: *southern Canada, the northern United States*

Height: *5 to 6.5 feet (1.50 to 2 m)*

Flowering: *April to May*

Properties: *antiseptic, energetic, galagtagogue, purgative*

Jerusalem artichoke

It is best to harvest the tubers always according to demand so that they are fresh and do not loose any of their aroma. Before being prepared, they are brushed thoroughly under running water to remove the dirt. After being soaked in water with lemon juice to prevent them from becoming discolored they are then cooked in salted water for approximately one quarter of an hour. There are many way to serve them: in a salad, sautéed with parsley and garlic, in ragouts, in gratins with béchamel sauce, in pies, purees and as fritters. Grated raw, they can be served with a vinaigrette or, seasoned with lemon, mixed in an endive or green salad with cheese. Jerusalem artichokes have a nutty taste similar to that of regular artichokes. In certain regions a spirit is distilled from its tubers.

The **Jerusalem artichoke** is a strong plant which was introduced to France in the 17th century by the Canadian governor **Samuel de Champlain** who noticed the nutritious importance of the tubers for the Huron and Algonquin Native Americans. He brought some tubers to Europe in the hope that this exotic vegetable could become acclimatized and be of use in times of famine. At the same time, the Tupinamba Indians from Brazil were being introduced to the French court. For some strange reason, the tubers were somehow associated with these indians and in France the tubers became known as "topinambour." The new vegetable, enthusiastically accepted by the people of the time, was completely rejected a century later.

In his "Traité de Jardinage," **de Combles** declared that the new vegetable was the worst of all vegetables. This was detrimental to the popularity of the **artichoke** which was soon replaced by the **potato**. To this day, this disliked vegetable is only found on the table in times of distress, like during World War II. However, recently it has quietly made its appearance once again on marketplaces. It is found under the names **Jerusalem artichoke** (derived from the Italian word "girasole" which means sunflower) or **Canadian artichoke**, a name which designates its true origin.

The part of the plant found above ground is a coarse perennial which can sometimes become invasive. It has a poorly branched out, hairy stem which carries big, oval, petioled leaves. The yellow, single flowers resemble in their appearance those of the sunflower, however, they are much smaller. They bear numerous achenes or fruit. The short underground root is frequently branched out with tubers growing from its end. The tubers resemble **potatoes** with an elongated shape and a yellowish or reddish coloring. Their juicy, firm, and sweet flesh is similar to that of **artichokes**.

Jerusalem artichokes grow on just about any soil. They are resistant to cold and thrive in the sun or in the shade. The plant is propagated by planting the tubers in the spring. Harvesting is often done in September; however, it is also possible to overwinter the tubers in the soil.

Jerusalem artichoke is rich in carbohydrates (15%), inulin (a substitute sugar for diabetics) and

fructose. In contrast, it is very low in proteins. The calorie content varies according to the length of storage. This vegetable increases the secretion of milk in nursing women and stimulates digestion.

The stems and leaves are used as a cattle feed. The tubers are also popular as pig fodder. **Jerusalem artichokes** are a beautiful decoration for gardens and their flowers can be used in floral arrangements.

HERACLEUM SPHONDYLIUM **Cow parsnip**
Leaf and fruit vegetable
Family: Umbelliferae
Origin: Europe
Height: 1.6 to 5 feet (0.50 to 1.50 m)
Flowering: June to September
Properties: aphrodisiac, tranquilizer, digestive, emmenagogue, hypotensive, (slightly) laxative, stimulant

Cow parsnip is a robust, wild plant used for a long time both as a vegetable and for its medicinal properties. Its leaves resemble the paws of a bear. It grows wild on meadows and in damp forests. It is a biennial plant with a rigid, hollow, hairy stem. Its grey-green lobed leaves are covered with very large, rough hairs. They are cut irregularly and give off an unpleasant smell when touched. The white, yellow or pink flowers form a big terminal inflorescence which bears flattened fruit with a big winged border. This plant has a bitter pungent and irritating taste. It is sown in the spring in heavy and moist soil. The parts of the plant that are used are the leaves, the fruit and the roots which are dried in the sun.

Cow parsnip is rich in carbohydrates, proteins, minerals, essential oils, and vitamin C. It also contains a substance which can increase the skin's sensitivity to light causing severe inflammations. It facilitates digestion and stimulates the menstrual flow. Because it contains vitamin C, it is also a stimulant. It is used in health spa therapies and to fight influenza and lower blood pressure. The seeds are quite stimulating and are considered an aphrodisiac.

In Poland, the leaves and seeds are cooked and fermented to produce a bitter beverage whose taste lies somewhere between beer and vegetable soup. The young leaves and shoots are cooked like vegetables and are served as a accompaniment to meat. They can also be mixed with other vegetables, cooked like **spinach**, added to stews, or as an ingredient in herbal pâtés. In Russia they are used to prepare the traditional borscht, or beetroot soup. The seeds are used to make delicious, soothing liqueurs which alleviate indigestion.

HORDEUM VULGARE — **Barley**
Fruit vegetable
Family: Gramineae
Origin: the Middle East
Height: about 16 inches (40 cm)
Flowering: spring
Properties: soothing, anti-diarrhoea, cardiotonic, emollient, sedative

---

Barley is adaptable to a greater range of climate than any other cereal, with varieties suited to temperate, subarctic, or subtropical areas. About half of the world's crop is used as livestock feed, the rest for malting and for food; however, rarely in the bakery. **Barley** flour, mixed with a little **wheat** flour, is however used to make an unleavened type of bread, or flatbread with a slightly bitter taste.

In former times, **barley** was easier to grow than wheat, and gave a marginally large yield per acre. However, it was neither as tasty nor as nutritious as wheat.

The plant has an upright, round hollow stem. Its hermaphrodite flowers stand in loose clusters. The unifloral ears appear in six rows having their spike notched on opposite sides, with three spikelets at each notch, each containing a small individual flower, or feathery floret, that develops a kernel. The kernels are oblong, green, open at the top with a longitudinal furrow.

There are several varieties of **barley**: **common barley** with six rows or **big barley**; six row **barley**, **square barley**, or **winter barley** with short, big ears; four-rowed **black barley**; two-rowed, **Spanish** or **Peruvian barley**; and **pyramid barley**, **German rice**, **false rice** or **Russian rice**, which is a very rare species with two-rowed, short ears.

Common barley is sown in winter, while the other varieties are sown in the early spring. Harvesting is done in the late summer.

Barley contains a lot of starch, 60% of carbohydrates, amino acids, lipids and cellulose. It is also a good source of minerals and vitamins B, D and E. The germinated seeds, known as malt, contain enzymes which transform starch into easily digestible substances. **Barley** is especially healthy for people with weak stomaches because it soothes the digestive tract. Its germ contains a protein, hordein, which accelerates heart rhythm and augments blood pressure just like adrenaline; therefore, it is a cardiotonic recommended for weak and slow hearts. Thanks to its emollient and sedative properties, a poultice of **barley** flour relieves bronchitis and angina.

IPOMOEA BATATAS — **Sweet potato**
Leaf and root vegetable
Family: Convolvulaceae
Origin: uncertain, known in Oceania for a very long time
Height: climbing, about 17 feet (5 m)
Flowering: spring
Properties: digestive, energizer, nutritious, mineralizing

Barley

Barley flour is used to make cakes, bread, milk puddings and porridges. The grain is offered finely ground, but is also crushed, or hulled and coarsely cracked as barley groats. Whole, peeled barley kernels are cooked like rice in salted water and served with vegetable dishes. To prepare desserts, they are cooked in milk. Cooked barley is used in stuffings and vinaigrette salads. Pearl barley consists of whole kernels from which the outer husk and part of the bran layer have been removed by a polishing process. A refreshing herbal tea is also made from barley. The roasted kernels are used to make a beverage similar to coffee. Most beer is made from malted barley. Furthermore, barley has a soft star used as livestock feed.

Known in Oceania as *kumara*, and in Peru as *kamar*, **sweet potato** is a staple food in these regions. It was introduced to Europe by **Christopher Columbus** and acclimatized by the Portuguese in Africa where it is also widely cultivated. Arab traders introduced it into Southeast Asia where it forms part of the everyday diet due to its nutritional properties. **Sweet potatoes** are considered to be one of the important food crops in the world. It has been theorized that the hard coat of the **sweet potato** seed enabled it to remain floating on the long passage from the coasts of Central America to the islands of the South Pacific.

Sweet potato stems are usually long and trailing and bear alternate, long stalked, spherical, generally green sometimes dark red leaves. The flowers, borne in clusters in the axils of the leaves, are funnel shaped and tinged with pink or rose violet. The fruit, or capsules, contain three or four black, dark seeds. The edible part is the much-enlarged tuberous root, varying in shape from fusiform to oblong or pointed oval. The tubers have a smooth, fine, dark yellow to violet rind and a white, yellow or orange, juicy flesh. In Europe the most popular varieties are: the pink, the white from Malaga, the purple from the Antilles, and the yellow with brown stripes. **Sweet potato** is not hardy to temperatures below 68 °F (20 °C). The plant is propagated vegetatively through sprouts arising from the roots or by cuttings of the vines which are planted in the spring. It is best adapted to light, friable soils. The plants grow very quickly and need a lot of water. They are harvested before the first frosts. One single plant yields approximately 4.4 to 6.6 lbs. (2 to 3 kg) of **sweet potatoes** which are kept in cold or dry storage.

Sweet potatoes contain many proteins, carbohydrates (10 to 15%), amino acids (5%), mineral salts and vitamins B and C. Because they have a considerable energetic value, they invigorate the organism. Moreover, they are easily digestible.

Sweet potatoes are prepared like **potatoes**. Cooked in water or sautéed they are used to make purees, gratins and soufflés. They can also be fried like French fries. In the United States they are served caramelized along with the Christmas roast. They are also used in salads. The fresh leaves, rich in vegetable proteins (like **soy bean** sprouts) are eaten raw in salads or cooked like **spinach** as a vegetable to accompany meat and fish. The remaining shoots and leaves are used as livestock feed.

Lettuce

Lettuce is usually eaten fresh in simple salads or mixed with other vegetables. The leaves can be used to garnish cold dishes, fish, meat and cheese. They are also used to prepare purees and creamy soups. They can also be stuffed with white meat and poultry. Blanched lettuce hearts can be prepared as a gratin with béchamel sauce and grated cheese.

LACTUCA SATIVA **Lettuce**
Leaf vegetable
Family: *Compositae*
Origin: *Europe*
Height: *4 to 8 inches (10 to 20 cm)*
Flowering: *June to September (from the second year)*
Properties: *soothing, analgesic, purgative, sedative*

Lettuce as we know it today probably derived from an improvement of the wild variety originating from Europe, known as *Lactuca virosa*. This vegetable, already known in ancient Egypt, Athens and Rome, is nowadays highly prized worldwide.

There are five principal varieties of **lettuce**: **cos** or **romaine lettuce** (without a doubt, one of the oldest); **butter head** or **cabbage lettuce**; **crisp head lettuce**; **asparagus lettuce**; and **leaf** or **curled lettuce**. All of these **lettuces** are hardy to cold. Most varieties have big, undivided leaves with smooth or wavy edges. The color varies according to sort. When there is a floral pedicel, the leaves are small and folded, and the stem is thick. At the head of the pedicel, the white or yellow flowers stand in small groups which form altogether a loose panicle. They bear flattened, dark purple achenes with thick edges. The root of the plant is fusiform with hardly any branches.

For successful cultivation **lettuce** requires ample water and shade, especially in warmer regions. **Spring lettuces** are sown in March; **winter** and **autumn lettuces** in April and June; and **summer lettuces** in August. **Romaine lettuces** are also sown from March to June and the **asparagus** variety from March until the end of August. Harvesting takes place when the heart is well formed by cutting it closely to the ground. **Lettuce** contains a lot of water (95%) and is very low in calories. Nevertheless, it contains a white latex which has a comforting and hypnotic effect. In former times, **lettuce** was used to disintoxicate opium addicts. It also contains fiber and cellulose which ease digestion. It is a good source of vitamins A, B, C and E. It is also used to alleviate inflammations and promote the regeneration of body tissue.

LAGENARIA SICERARIA   **Bottle or Calabash gourd**

Fruit vegetable
Family: Cucurbitaceae
Origin: Africa
Height: climbing and creeping, several feet
Blooming time: spring
Properties: soothing, laxative, sedative

The strange fruit of the **bottle gourd** were already used in prehistoric times as a vegetable and in the production of utensils and containers. They are also known as calabash, even though they are not even remotely related to this tree which is native to tropical America. In Morocco and in many other African countries, these **gourds** are a staple crop.

This creeping or climbing monoecious, vine, with a hairy stem and long forked tendrils has large, round, heart shaped basal leaves. The large, showy white flowers have an undivided calyx. Female flowers have a long cylindrical ovary, while the male ones have long peduncles. They bear edible fruit which vary greatly in size and shape. Most **bottle gourds** have a thick, shell which is tender when young and hard, water proof and very resistant when ripe. Their flesh contains numerous flat, elongated seeds. However, there is a variety whose shell is particularly soft at first and whose flesh does not become bitter, and which is eaten as a vegetable. They

are generally sown in April and transplanted in May. The plant grows very quickly and must be watered frequently. The young fruit are harvested once they reach a good size but before they are ripe.

Bottle gourds contain 90% water and very few calories. They are rich in vitamin A, some vitamin C, fiber, and minerals like calcium and potassium. This vegetable has a delicate fragrance and a pleasant flavor. It has a soothing effect on mucous membranes, alleviates inflammations and relieves anxiety. Because it is high in fibers, it facilitates digestion and the elimination of toxins.

Bottle gourds are eaten cooked in soups or purees, in gratins or rissoles. In North Africa they are an ingredient in couscous; in Japan they are cut in small pieces, dried and used to give flavor to soups all year round. When harvested ripe, almost dry, their flesh is removed and they are left to dry in order to make utensils, containers and musical instruments.

LENS ESCULENTA   **Lentils**

Fruit vegetable
Family: Fabaceae
Origin: the Middle East
Height: 12 to 14 inches (30 to 35 cm)
Flowering: late spring
Properties: emollient, purifier, laxative, mineralizing

Lentils are among the oldest vegetables to have been cultivated by mankind, reaching back into prehistory. Lentils have been food at archaeological digs dating from the Neolithic Age. Their cultivation probably started at around 7,000 BC in the Middle East. **Lentil** seeds have been found in Egyptian burials from the time of the Pharaohs. The Romans let the lentils germinate before using them in order to obtain a sweeter taste.

A long time ago only two varieties of **lentils** were cultivated. Today, many different sorts are being grown and traded: the green **Puy lentil** is one of the most popular; the **blond lentil** is the biggest; and the **Egyptian orange lentil,** which does not have a husk and is consumed foremost in Italy and Germany, to name but a few.

This small annual legume forms weak, long ascending stems with pinnate, narrow alternate leaves

---

Lentils

Before preparing lentils, they first have to be carefully sorted out in order to remove unwanted grit and impurities, and then soaked overnight in fresh water. Usually they are cooked in salted water with baking soda, chopped onions and cloves. They can be served cold in a salad or warm with bacon and sausages, in a soup or a puree. They can be prepared in Romany style by adding pepper, cumin, vinegar, sage, mint, parsley and saffron to the cooking water.

which have six pairs of oblong, linear leaflets ending in a spine. The single, filiform peduncles appear on the axils of the leaves each one carrying one to four terminal white flowers finely striped in blue. The fruit produce broadly oblong and slightly inflated pods which contain two seeds the shape of a doubly convex lens. These seeds are consumed as a vegetable.

Lentils thrive best in dry, sandy, but fertile soil. Because they need a lot of warmth, in temperate regions they are sown directly onto the field in the late spring. They are harvested in the late summer once the shoots are almost dry. **Lentils** are a good source of protein, vitamin B, mineral salts, and a lot of iron and phosphorus. **Lentils** are a very nutritious vegetable which soothe intestinal inflammation and reduce the danger of abscesses. Germinated lentils are used in some regions as a decoration for nativity scenes.

LEPIDIUM SATIVUM **Garden cress**
Leaf vegetable
Family: Cruciferae
Origin: western Asia
Height: 8 to 12 inches (20 to 30 cm)
Flowering: spring
Properties: anti-scurvy, apéritif, purifier, digestive, diuretic, stimulant

---

Garden cress was for a long time forgotten and is now being rediscovered by vegetarians who appreciate its taste and medical properties. It is a fast growing herb which can be easily cultivated in the garden and on the balcony. This delicate annual plant with finely pinnate foliage is sown in early spring.

There are two varieties: a common variety with simple leaves and another, more original, with curly leaves. According to taste they are cultivated in two different ways. They can be deeply sown in order to quickly obtain a tuft of herbs to season salads, meat, or cheese and which are harvested once they reach a height of 2 to 6 inches (5 to 15 cm). The advantage of the close seeding is that the **garden cress** germinates more quickly. To harvest the plant all year round, the sowing can be spread out and done several times. The second method consists of sowing it in rows. Once the plants are strong enough, they are thinned out at a distance of 4 to 8 inches (10 to 20 cm) from one another. In this way, the seeds can be sown either in the spring or the summer

and harvested in the autumn. To prosper well, **garden cress** needs plenty of water and in summer a shady place.

Garden cress contains vitamin A and a lot of vitamin C. It is a good tonic for the body, prevents viral diseases, colds, scurvy and fatigue. Its peppery taste is due to the essential oils it contains. **Garden cress** stimulates the appetite and facilitates digestion. Its juice revitalizes nails and hair.

LYCOPERSICUM ESCULENTUM **Tomato**
Fruit vegetable
Family: Solanaceae
Origin: South America
Height: over 6 feet (2 m)
Flowering: late spring
Properties: soothing, apéritif, anti-arthritis, anti-inflammatory, diuretic, laxative, revitalizing

---

Today **tomatoes** are a worldwide favorite vegetable available all year round. **Tomato** plants are annual and generally very branched and recumbent when fruiting, but a few forms are compact and upright. Its long stalked leaves are more or less hairy, strongly odorous, and pinnately compound. The flowers are yellow and disposed on terminal pending clusters. They bear large fruit or voluminous, smooth skinned berries usually red, scarlet, or yellow; which vary in shape from almost spherical through oval and elongate to pear-shaped. The thick, juicy pulp is segmented in chambers containing many cells of small, flat seeds. The whole plant releases a strong aromatic fragrance. There are at least a hundred different varieties of **tomatoes** with different shapes, sizes and colors.

Tomatoes need soil rich in humus with sufficient humidity. Light soil is preferable for early **tomatoes** and heavier soil for late ones. The plants are rather sensitive and need a warm, sunny location which is protected from the wind. In February, they are sown in beds in the greenhouse. Once the plants reach a height of 6 inches (15 cm) and there is no more danger of frosts, they can be planted in the field at intervals of 16 inches (40 cm) from each other and propped. As the plant develops, the buds that form on the leaf axils are cut off. Harvesting begins when the fruit are ripe and very colorful. Green **tomatoes** which are large enough can be set to ripen indoors.

Cress
The peppery young leaves of the cress are a delicious garnish for salads, meat and fish. They enhance sandwiches and cold cuts. Older leaves can be cooked in soups, purees, soufflés and gratins.

Ripe **tomatoes** can be dried, pickled in olive oil canned, whole or pureed. **Tomatoes** contain a lot of water (90%) as well as some sugar (3 to 4%). They are rich in vitamin A, vitamin C, vitamin B9, mineral salts, such as potassium, magnesium and phosphorus, as well as trace elements. Their red coloring comes from a pigment, lycopene, which is similar to carotene. Green **tomatoes** contain the toxic alkaloid solanine.

Tomatoes have a calming effect on tissue and alleviate inflammations. They are recommended for people suffering from arthritis. They help in the production of urine, and because they contain folic acid, they promote the formation of red blood cells. Moreover, they stimulate digestion. **Tomatoes** revitalize the skin protecting it from the sun. Despite all this, it is the only vegetable whose parts are not all assimilated by the body: its skin and seeds are not digestible.

MANIHOT ESCULENTA	**Cassava, Yuca, Mandioc, Manioc**

Root vegetable
Family: Euphorbiaceae
Origin: Brazil, northern South America
Height: 1.50 to 6.5 feet (2 m)
Blooming time: summer
Properties: soothing, digestive, nutritious, mineralizing, tonic

---

This perennial shrub, also known as **mandioc** or **manioc**, is a staple food in Central and South America where it is called *yucca*, even though the plant is not related to the ornamental plant of the lily family with the same name. **Cassava** is found growing wild in Mexico and in the Amazon area. **Cassava** consumption spread to the African continent where its culture quickly developed, particularly in Nigeria, Zaire, Tanzania, Ghana, Uganda, Mozambique and Madagascar. Today, the plant is grown and consumed in most tropical regions of the world.

The **cassava** root is tuberous with a beige brown skin and a white flesh. According to the variety it can weigh between 4.4 lbs. (2 kg) and 44 lbs. (20 kg). Its petioled leaves are dark green, palmate and deeply parted into five to nine lobes. The monoecious flowers appear in terminal clusters. They have a reddish, bell-shaped calyx with five lobes and no corolla. The male flowers have ten stamens standing on the edge of a fleshy disk. The female flowers have an ovary with three

chambers. They bear globular fruit with a single seed which disintegrates while splitting in three.

The fleshy roots are the parts of the plant which are harvested. These roots contain, like the rest of the plant, a cyanide-producing sugar derivative (hydrocyanic acid) which is highly poisonous. To remove the poison, the tubers must be rubbed and dried in the sun or cooked. Because the poison is highly volatile, it is not resistant to air or heat.

Cassava thrives in average, deep soil in a warm, damp region. It is planted deep in the earth, and after a year it already has root tubers the size of a big **beetroot**. From this point on it can be harvested upon demand. The roots of this plant can remain in the soil from 8 to 24 months without rotting. **Cassava** contains mainly starch and latex, but it also has some amino acids, minerals, calcium, magnesium, vitamin B and small amounts of vitamin C. When prepared in the right way, it is a healthy and very digestive food which soothes inflammations and strengthens the organism.

MEDICAGO SATIVA	**Alfalfa sprouts**

Leaf vegetable
Family: Fabaceae
Origin: Central Europe
Height: 12 to 16 inches (30 to 40 cm)
Flowering: late spring
Properties: mineralizing, stimulant

Also called lucerne or purple medic, **alfalfa sprouts** are very refreshing and appetizing. They are found in small, tight patches of germinated seeds approximately 2 to 6 inches (5 to 15 cm) high, like **garden cress**. The plant arises from a much-branched crown that is partially embedded in the surface layer of soil. As the plant develops, numerous thin stems bearing many trifoliolate leaves arise from the crown buds. Racemes of small, pale purple flowers arise from the upper axillary buds of the stems. They bear corkscrew coiled pods containing from two to eight or more seeds.

Alfalfa is grown in greenhouses, on the balcony, or in the garden. The plant needs a light soil of average quality, not too much sun exposure and plenty of water. They are sown in the spring directly in the open land or in pots. Most seeds germinate within six days and are harvested once they reach the necessary height.

Tomato

Contrary to what one might assume, it was not the Italians who invented tomato sauce, but rather the Indians living in Central America who seasoned it with different kinds of bell peppers. Today there are a multiplicity of tomato sauces to accompany pasta, meat and fish. Fresh tomatoes can be prepared in salads or stuffed with a mixture of mayonnaise and chopped vegetables. They can be cooked with parsley and garlic or stuffed with meat. Tomatoes are an ingredient in the traditional ratatouille niçoise, in gratins, in fish and seafood recipes and in different eastern dishes. Green tomatoes are used in omelettes and to prepare chutney. Tomato juice is a delicious apéritif, preferably with a dash of Tabasco sauce.

Alfalfa sprouts contain proteins (55%), amino acids, vitamins A, B and C. Other contents are mineral salts, particularly calcium, as well as trace elements (like iron, phosphorus, zinc, copper and silicon) and a vegetable estrogen.

Alfalfa sprouts are recommended for people suffering from anaemia and nervous exhaustion. They strengthen fingernails and hair. The hormonal effect of their vegetable estrogen combined with the silicon and calcium they contain, helps fight against menopausal symptoms as well as osteoporosis.

Alfalfa sprouts are eaten raw in salads. They are used to give flavor to sandwiches and as a garnish for meat, fish, eggs and omelettes.

MESEMBRYANTHEMUM CRYSTALLINUM — **Ice plant, Sea fig, Sea marigold**

Leaf vegetable
Family: Aizoaceae
Origin: South Africa
Height: 24 to 32 inches (60 to 80 cm)
Blooming time: summer
Properties: sour, laxative, diuretic, emollient, tonic

Also known as **sea fig** or **sea marigold**, this perennial plant was forgotten for a long time. Today it is again being used for its culinary, medicinal and decorative properties.

The plant has long stems with numerous fleshy, round leaves which are covered by transparent, glistening glands containing a salty liquid. Because of these glands, the plant glitters in the sun, as if it were covered with ice-crystals. The delicate ray flowers come in a variety of colors. They form hard, pentagonal fruit. The leaves, which are the part of the plant that is consumed, have a refreshing, sour taste.

The plant thrives in light, moist, sandy soil. It does not endure constant humidity, but does well in warm, arid areas, tolerating the full sun almost as a cactus does. It is cultivated either by cuttings or by superficial seeding directly onto the field from spring to summer. The leaves are harvested fresh according to demand during the whole summer. The **ice plant** has 95% water and is low in calories. However, it is rich in vitamins A, B and C, mineral salts and trace elements. Due to its sour taste, this vegetable is very refreshing a good thirst quencher. The plant stimulates liver activity,

Cassava

There are many different ways of preparing cassava. Cassava is obtained by rubbing the fresh root and later squeezing and drying it with a cloth in order to eliminate most of the poisonous substance it contains. This puree is then spread out in the sun to dry. The paste is thinly sliced and cooked over high heat. These cookies or toasts are eaten like bread, added to soups, vegetable stews and meat or fish dishes. They can also be made into very puffy fritters. Cassava can be kept in dry storage for many years without spoiling. Tapioca, or cassava starch, is made from mashing, roasting and grinding the roots. An alcoholic beverage, known as mobi, is made by fermenting cassava water with grated sweet potatoes and molasses syrup. The latex sap of cassava cooked for several hours over low heat with salt and pepper produces a Creole sauce known as cabiou used to enhance meat and fish.

promotes the production of bile juice, and is a diuretic. **Ice plant** is consumed raw, cut in salads or cooked to accompany meat or in purees and soups. It is also a beautiful addition to any rock garden.

MOMORDICA BALSAMINA — **Wild cucumber, Balsam apple**

Fruit vegetable
Family: Cucurbitaceae
Origin: tropical regions of America and of Asia
Height: 1.6 feet (1.50 m)
Flowering: spring
Properties: emetic, purgative, purifier, rubefacient, vulnerary

---

This ancient vegetable is quite popular in India. It is a annual climber with delicate, striped stems and simple tendrils. The palmate leaves are deeply lobed in three to five lobes whose edges are roughly dented. The small yellow, single, male and female flowers bear large, oval fruit which hang from a long peduncle. Their appearance resemble that of a big, round **cucumber**. Young fruit are at first green, then shinny orange as they ripen. The ripe fruit split open lengthways into two to three segments releasing numerous seeds. Even after seeding, this is a very decorative plant.

Its fleshy rind encloses a juicy red pulp which has a particular, sour and bitter taste. To prosper well, the plant needs a lot of humidity and warmth. The seeds are sown in the spring in average soil with a support so that the plant can climb. The fruits are harvested, when they are still green and young, before their bitterness becomes too strong and while the seeds are not too hard.

Wild cucumber contains a lot of water and a bitter substance known as cucurbacine. Even though it is low in calories, the plant is a good tonic for a weak organism. Externally applied, it helps heal small wounds and bruises. It also contains fatty acids, mineral salts, and vitamins B and C. This vegetable also has cleansing effect on the organism – it removes poisons and calms inflammations. In the pharmacy it is used to prepare ointments for haemorrhoids.

The fruit are consumed cooked as a accompaniment for meat and fish. In China the seeds of a related variety, *Momordica cochinchinensis*, are used to produce an oil for burning, while the roots are used to make soap. An African variety, *Momordica foetida*, contains a substance used in the treatment of diabetes.

ORYZA SATIVA   Rice
Fruit vegetable
Family: *Gramineae*
Origin: *India, Asia*
Height: *1.6 to 5 feet (0.50 to 1.50 m)*
Blooming time: *spring*
Properties: *soothing, anti-diarrhoea, hypotensive*

It is assumed that the cultivation of **rice** began in China about 2,800 BC, and in India around 2,300 BC. As contact with India increased its use quickly spread, so that by the time of **Alexander the Great** it was already being consumed by the inhabitants of Macedonia and Mesopotamia, as well as by those of Egypt and Persia. It was not untill the 8th century however, that Arab traders brought it to Spain, from where it later spread to southern Europe.

This annual grass is cultivated in the tropical, semitropical and temperate regions of the world. Its leaves are long, sharp and flattened with very rough edges and deeply split sheaths. It has a fasciculate root, i.e. without a central pivot. The hermaphrodite flowers form a more or less, terminal panicle, or inflorescence, made up of spikelets bearing flowers that produce the fruit, or grain. The grains are compact, streaked and generally oblong. These seeds can be classified in two large groups: the "indica," which is long, slim and pigmented with different hues; and the "Japonica," which is round to oval, smaller with a short stem.

There are several different types of **rice** of which the most well known are **Thai rice**, **American rice**, **Surinam rice**, **Basmati rice**, **Italian round rice**, **full grain rice**, and **perfumed rice**, among others. The **wild rice** growing in North America and India belongs to a variety known as *Zizania aquatica*. This grass is not related to **rice**, but its grain, often considered a delicacy, is rich in proteins and fiber.

Rice is cultivated from seed in the spring in wet or inundated land. In the autumn, the seedlings are transplanted to an enclosed field, or paddy, which stands under water. After 100 to 180 days, the harvest begins. Earlier **rice** was picked by hand. Today the plants are harvested mechanically from the paddy fields. Under optimal conditions, harvesting can be done three to four times per year. It is the cereal crop with the greatest yield per acre in the world. **Brown rice** is rich in starch and vitamin B1. Besides, it contains minerals, magnesium and proteins (8%). **Rice** is a good energy source

which reduces high blood pressure. **White rice** is easier to digest and is recommended for people suffering from ulcers or dyspepsia. Its cooking water soothes the stomach and prevents irritation. The seeds mashed to a powder are used as soothing poultices.

Rice flour is used in cosmetics industry to make **rice** powder. The straw is used to manufacture cigarette paper and other fine papers.

PACHYRHIZUS EROSUS   Jicama, Yam bean
Root, fruit or pod vegetable
Family: *Fabaceae*
Origin: *Central America, Mexico, Eastern and South-East Asia*
Height: *about 16 feet (5 m)*
Flowering: *spring*
Properties: *soothing, purifier, diuretic, purgative*

Jicama is a leguminous vine native to Mexico which grows in tropical regions and has been cultivated by the people of Central and South America for years. Altogether there are six varieties, three are grown for food: *Pachyrhizus erosus* is the most popular in Asia and America, *Pachyrhizus ahipa* is cultivated in Bolivia and Argentina, and *Pachyrhizus tuberosus* with its large roots is found in the whole Amazon basin.

The plant has thick roots with irregularly globular, brown-skinned, white fleshed, crisp, and juicy tubers. The leaves consist of three single, ovoid leaflets and are dented or lobed. The exterior leaflets can reach 6 inches (15 cm) in length, while the middle ones can be up to 8 inches (20 cm) long. The blue or white purple inflorescence appear in terminal clusters and are covered with numerous butterfly flowers which bear the fruit or seedpods. These are about 6 inches (15 cm) long, covered with fine, dense hairs and contain four to nine brownish seeds. The parts of the plant which are harvested are the pods and the juicy tubers.

Jicama thrives in warm, damp regions. The roots are planted in the autumn in rich soil at the base of a solid prop to enable the plant to climb. It grows fast and problem free.

The fruit are harvested once they are formed, and consumed as a vegetable immediately as they cannot be conserved. The tubers are pulled out nine months after being planted to be consumed young, fresh and juicy, or left until the following spring when used for their starch. Once harvested, the tubers are kept in dry, dark storage.

Rice
Rice is cooked in water and served as a side dish to other foods. It is an ingredient in salads and vegetable stuffings. It is prepared with tomatoes, aromatic herbs, and is the main ingredient for risotto. It can also be cooked with oil and stock. It is added to omelettes and fritters. As a dessert it is cooked in milk and an ingredient in cakes and puddings. The grains can be eaten caramelized and puffed. Rice flour is used to make noodles of different sorts and biscuits. The grain can also be distilled to prepare a spirit known as arrak, or fermented to produce the rice wine known as sake in Japan.

Jicama has a high water content (80 %) and very few calories. It contains fiber, proteins (10%), carbohydrates, vitamins A and C, minerals and trace elements. When mature the tubers become very fibrous and are very rich in starch. They are a good diuretic, sooth the stomach and are easily digestible.

The young tubers are eaten raw in salads or cooked with fish and meat, in purees, gratins, or fried with **parsley** and garlic. In Thailand they are cooked with chili peppers, sugar, and salt. The young tender pods are prepared like string-beans. The starch extracted from the old tubers is used to prepare an alternative to arrow-root which is used in soups and crêpes.

PANICUM MILIACEUM　　　*Millet*
Fruit vegetable
Family: *Gramineae*
Origin: *probably India*
Height: *20 to 32 inches (50 to 80 cm)*
Blooming time: *spring*
Properties: *anti-anaemia, anti-cholesterol, diuretic, nutritious*

Millet is considered one of the oldest cereals on earth. Archaeological finds have shown that it was cultivated in China and Mesopotamia around 5,000 BC. However, today, millions of men, women and children in Central Asia and southern Siberia still rely on it for their sustenance.

This annual plant has a stem with nodules that enable it to regenerate itself quickly. Its green, alternate leaves are thin and enclosed by sheaths. The inconspicuous, hermaphrodite, green or violet flowers are borne on terminal racemes. These flowers bear fruit or caryopsis that remain enclosed in husks without releasing the small, round, yellow, white or black seeds.

Millet prospers on loose soil and is resistant to drought. The seeds are sown in April or May on dry soil. **Millet** is rich in carbohydrates, proteins and minerals. It also contains fiber and vitamins B, D, and E. Its nutritive value can be compared to that of **wheat**. The fiber content of **millet** speeds and stimulates the digestive process and the elimination of unused and indigestible foods. Moreover, it reduces the risk of cancer. Its germ contains fatty acids that protect against cardio-vascular disease.

Millet is also used as birdseed and in chicken-feed mixtures.

Millet

Millet is used to prepare tasty and digestive porridges. It is also used to make unleaven breads that are eaten either with jelly or cracked in soups. Germinated millet seeds are used in salads or to garnish sandwiches and cold cuts. Millet seed is also well known as a food for pet birds in the home, and for poultry on the farm.

PASTINACA SATIVA　　　*Parsnip*
Root vegetable
Family: *Umbelliferae*
Origin: *Eurasia*
Height: *16 to 24 inches (40 to 60 cm)*
Flowering: *July to August*
Properties: *purifier, diuretic, sedative*

This ancient vegetable which had a high reputation among Roman gourmets was widely replaced by the **carrot** during the 11th century, although in Great Britain it remained a much loved staple food. Recently, vegetable lovers in other countries have rediscovered it and have brought it back to the table. This biennial plant resistant to cold has an upright, hollow, grooved stem, and compound leaves with oval, lobed, hairy and dented leaflets. Its yellow flowers, which appear in large umbels, bear smooth, splendid, round to oval fruit. **Parsnip** is cultivated for its large, tapering, fleshy white edible root which has a soft, sweet and aromatic taste. **Parsnip** thrives in damp, deep, rather heavy soil in sunny areas. It is sown directly onto the field from February to June. In very mild regions, it can be sown until the end of September. Harvesting of the roots is done four months after the sowing. However, the roots may remain in the soil during the winter months; exposure to low temperatures makes the roots sweeter. **Parsnip** contains water, sugar, an essential oil, proteins and vitamin C. **Parsnip** is a good source of energy while stimulating the digestive system. It is also a tranquilizer. The young roots are usually eaten raw and grated to sweeten, refresh and flavor salads.

PETROSELINUM CRISPUM VAR. TUBERSOSUM

Turnip-rooted parsley

Root vegetable
Family: Umbelliferae
Origin: Mediterranean basin
Height: 8 to 12 cm (20 to 30 cm)
Flowering: summer
Properties: anti-anaemia, anti-scurvy, apéritif, purifier, diuretic, emmenagogue, sedative, stimulant, tonic

---

There are two varieties: **Hamburg parsley** or **turnip-rooted parsley** whose root is a vegetable; and **common parsley** whose leaves are used as a flavoring and a garnish. This hardy biennial plant has a large, white parsniplike root with a delicate flavor. Its stem is branched, streaked, and full of nodules with compound, deep green, tender and curled or deeply frilled leaves. The seed stalks are topped by compound umbels of small, yellow flowers which bear oval, greenish yellow fruit. **Turnip-rooted parsley** thrives in fresh, light soil that is rich in humus and partly sunny. The young, juicy roots which were sown in the spring are harvested in the summer; while the larger ones are pulled out in the autumn.

Turnip-rooted parsley contains fiber, water, sugar, apiol – an essential oil – iron, calcium, phosphorous and high amounts of vitamins A and C. Because of its ability to ease muscle cramps it is used as a digestive aid. It is also prescribed as a mild diuretic.

PHASEOLUS VULGARIS

Bean

Fruit vegetable
Family: Fabaceae
Origin: South America
Height: from 1 to 8 feet (0.40 to 2.50 m), depending on the variety
Flowering: late spring, summer
Properties: soothing, purifier, diuretic, stimulant, tonic

This dwarf or semiclimbing **bean** plant has long, petioled, green leaves with three oval and pointed leaflets. The white flowers have five petals with six stamens whose long pistil covers the growing fruit or pod. These pods are formed by two valves containing the seeds which generally have a thick shell when ripe. The size and shape of the seeds vary depending on the type of **bean**.

Beans grow well in light, fresh soil without too much lime and not too humid. They are very sensitive to cold and require a sunny, warm location. They must not be cultivated too early in the season; therefore, sowing takes place at the end of spring directly onto the field. After twenty days, the shoots are trimmed and artificial supports are set up for the climbing varieties. Harvesting differs according to variety. **Green** or **string beans** are harvested when the pods are green or pale yellow and young; **haricot beans** are harvested once they are ripe when the **beans** are well formed but still tender, or, when they are very ripe and almost dry. Dried **haricot beans** can be preserved a long time in storage; **green beans** are bottled or frozen.

Green beans are low in calories and contain water, fiber, amino acids, vitamins A, B, C and E as well as mineral salts (calcium and iron). Dried **haricot beans** contain carbohydrates (11%), amino acids, fiber (5%), trace elements (iron, magnesium calcium, phosphorus and iodine), vitamins A, C, E, and all vitamins of the B group. **Green beans** have a positive effect on the digestive tract and adjust the cholesterol level in the blood. They contain a substance which balances metabolic disorders, protects the liver and strengthens the heart. They also lower the absorption of glucose in people suffering from diabetes. Dried **haricot beans** possess an element that promotes formation of new white blood cells after treatment with antibiotics. **Beans** strengthen the organism and are recommended during convalescence.

PHYLLOSTACHYS HETEROCYCLA

Bamboo (Sprouts)

Stem vegetable
Family: Gramineae
Origin: Asia
Height: depending on the variety, 26 to 82 feet (8 to 25 m)
Flowering: late spring
Properties: purifier, mineralizing, stimulant, tonic

Parsnip

The raw parsnip root, grated or thinly sliced is delicious when served with a vinaigrette as a delicate, fragrant hors-d'œuvre. Cooked in salted water it can be used alone or mixed with other vegetables as a side dish. Roasted together with a joint of meat, or simply deep fried, it is a delicious addition to any meal. It can also be used to prepare delightful purees. Its intensely fragrant leaves are used as a seasoning in soups and salads.

Bamboo, known in China, India and Japan for its medicinal properties, is a staple food in Asia. **Bamboos** are used for a variety of purposes: the small stems are used to produce several utensils while the larger ones are used in construction; the pulped fibers are used to make fine quality paper; its leaves are a useful fodder for livestock.

Bamboos are giant, fast-growing grasses with woody, hollow, aerial stems or culms. These culms grow in branching clusters from a thick underground rhizome. The culms often form a dense undergrowth that excludes other plants. Mature **bamboos** sprout horizontal branches that bear sword shaped, small, alternate leaves on stalked blades; the leaves on young culms arise directly from the stem which is green, thick and marked with stigmata. **Bamboo** flowers are hardly noticeable. The sprouts and shoots of the plant are edible.

Bamboo thrives in rich, moist soil and is distributed in tropical and subtropical to mild temperate regions. It is hardy to cold and warm weather conditions alike. It is propagated through its spurs which are quickly replanted on rich soil. The shoots have a low calorific value, however, they contain proteins, sugar, numerous mineral salts like silicon, phosphorus and calcium, as well as different vitamins. The fine grained silica produced in the joint stems has been used as a medicine in China and India for centuries under the name *tabasheer*. Other varieties contain a toxic substance known as hydrogen cyanide which dissipates with cooking. **Bamboo** is used in medicine to treat joint and back pain. It promotes the formation of cartilage destroyed by arthritis or other articulatory diseases. It has a mineralizing effect on the body, relieving menopausal problems and preventing osteoporosis.

The shoots cooked in water are eaten in salads, soups, stuffings, sauces, and **rice**. Because **bamboo** shoots perish quickly, they are only found fresh in Asia.

There are a wide variety of **pea** plants including dwarf, half-dwarf, trailing, smooth-seeded, wrinkled-seeded which is sweet and very common, black-eyed, and **sugar peas** which produce edible pods considered to be a green legume.

The **pea** plant is a hardy, leafy annual with hollow trailing or climbing stems that end in tendrils which facilitate climbing. Its compound and pinnate leaves have three pairs of oval leaflets. The reddish or white flowers, growing two to three per stalk, are butterfly shaped. They bear a many-seeded fruit or pod that grows up to 4 inches (10 cm) long, splitting in half when ripe. Inside the pod, 5 to 10 seeds are attached by short stalks. These seeds are the edible parts of the plant.

The pods which are covered by green, juicy husks have a hard inner skin which makes them inedible. Only the sugar pea or *Pisum sativum* variety *saccharatum* is cultivated not for its seeds, but for its tender, flat sweet pods.

Peas should be planted in fertile, well drained soil in an unshaded spot. Sowing is done from February to June: early maturing **peas** are sown first, then **sugar peas** and finally wrinkle-seeded varieties which are the latest and sweetest ones. Three weeks later, the shoots are trimmed and supports are set up to facilitate climbing. **Sugar peas** are harvested first, followed by the most rounded ones, and finally the wrinkle-seeded ones. Rounded **peas** are harvested once the seeds are ripe and hard. Then their husks are removed.

Peas are rich in carbohydrates, amino acids, lipids (1.5%) and mineral salts (3%), like phosphorus and iron.

Peas are very nutritious. Fresh **peas** contain amino acids, phosphorus and vitamins A, B1, B2 and D. They also have a high nutritional value. This vegetable is recommended for people suffering from anaemia and during convalescence.

Peas

Chopped up, dried peas are used to prepare creamy soups and delicate, sweet purees which are generally served with pork and sausages. Fresh peas can be cooked with carrots, small onions, lettuce, thyme and bay leaves to be served as a side dish for meat and poultry. Sugar peas are cooked whole in water and served in a salad or sautéed with onions and tomatoes as an accompaniment to omelettes and meat.

PISUM SATIVUM   **Pea, Sugar pea**
Fruit vegetable
Family: *Fabaceae*
Origin: *central Europe and western Asia*
Height: *6.5 feet (2 m)*
Flowering: *spring*
Properties: *purifier, mineralizing, emollient, tonic*

RAPHANUS SATIVUS   **Radish**
Root vegetable
Family: *Cruciferae*
Origin: *unknown*
Height: *4 to 14 inches (10 to 35 cm)*
Flowering: *summer*
Properties: *anti-scurvy, apéritif, expectorant, laxative, diuretic, tonic*

This annual plant has a fleshy, spherical root with fan shaped, hairy leaves which are split into elongated segments the ends of which are round. The flowers, which have four white petals with a purple veining, bear fruit or siliques containing numerous small brown seeds. The **black radish** variety (*Raphanus niger*) has a large root with a rugged black rind and white flesh; it has a characteristic taste. The **Japanese radish** or **daikon** has a very long root that can weigh a few pounds; it has a very sweet taste.

Radish thrives in sunny and half-shady locations, preferably in a nourishing, deep soil which is not too stony. It is sown directly onto the field from March until the end of September according to variety. The soil must be kept moist and irrigated regularly. Generally **radishes** are harvested early before they become too large, roughly three weeks after being sown. **Black radishes** are sown onto the field from June to July, and are harvested in the autumn. After the harvest, the plant is left to dry in the sun for a day. The leaves are then cut off and the roots are placed in cool, well aired storage.

Radish contains water, aromatic oil and few calories. Nevertheless, it contains plenty of vitamins A, B and C, mineral salts (iron, iodine, phosphorus, magnesium and sulphur). **Radishes** are used to improve the hair, the skin and the nails. Thanks to their vitamin C content, they help prevent scurvy and influenza. They are diuretic and relieve bladder and liver problems. Their aromatic oil stimulates the appetite. **Radishes** are often recommended for people suffering from diabetes.

Radish

Raw radishes with salt or in a salad have a pungent, crisp, peppery taste. Japanese radish is also eaten raw in salads or grated to marinate fish. It is cooked like turnip and served as a side dish to meat and poultry. The leaves are used to season stews. Its young flowers are eaten like broccoli. The immature fruit or siliques are deliciously crisp, juicy and peppery sweet. The ripe seeds are used like mustard seeds. The whole plant can be used in the kitchen. Radish syrup is used to decongest the respiratory system.

RHEUM RHAPONTICUM	**Rhubarb**
Stem vegetable	
Family: *Polygonaceae*	
Origin: *probably central Asia*	
Height: *about 24 inches (60 cm)*	
Flowering: *late spring*	
Properties: *apéritif, tonic, laxative*	

The origin of **rhubarb** is unclear. Some assume that it comes from Tibet or Mongolia, others believe, it originated on the banks of the Volga. From very early times the Chinese have used the plant primarily as a cathartic. **Rhubarb** was not cultivated in Europe until it arrived via India and Asia Minor during the 18th century. However, it quickly became renowned as a healthy, delicate addition to the diet. This large, hardy perennial is one of the vegetables available early in the season. **Rhubarb** has a thick, fleshy taproot with large clumps of big, smooth leaves strongly waved at their base with a long, thick, reddish petiole. A large central flower stalk may appear and bear numerous small, reddish white flowers and angular, winged fruit containing one seed. Usually the inflorescence is cut off, so that the plant does not loose strength of growth.

Rhubarb is a very undemanding plant; it thrives without problem in partly sunny areas in deep, moist soil with good drainage. **Rhubarb** is propagated by division of the stumps in autumn which are then covered during the winter months. They can also be replanted and covered with hay and a cask. During the first year, the plant is left to grow without harvesting so that it becomes strong. During the second year, after being forced for four weeks, the oldest petioles can be harvested: they are taken from the basis and pulled away by twisting them off the plant. The plants can be harvested for up to ten years.

Rhubarb contains a lot of calcium oxalate. It is rich in vitamins and fiber. Its root contains anthracite glycosides which give it its purgative properties and its color.

Because **rhubarb** contains calcium oxalate, which gives it its characteristic grittiness, it is definitely not recommended for people who suffer from lithiasis, gout and rheumatism. Its fiber content has a mildly stimulating effect on the intestine, and its sour taste stimulates the appetite.

SALICORNIA EUROPAEA **Goosefoot**

Family: *Chenopodiaceae*
Origin: *coasts of the English Channel and the Atlantic ocean*
Height: *8 to 20 inches (20 to 50 cm)*
Flowering: *late summer*
Properties: *tranquilizer, emollient, laxative, stimulant, tonic*

This annual plant grows in salty terrain. Today, this plant is once again fashionable and can generally be found in fish shops.

This grey, green weed has thick, juicy, leafy stems with tiny, almost invisible, terminal flowers. Its root is woody. The sprouts are harvested young, tender and crisp before blooming in May, when they become woody and hard. They have a salty herbal taste.

Goosefoot is rich in mineral salts like calcium, magnesium, iodine and iron. It has few calories. It has some amino acids, sugar and fiber which have a positive effect on the digestive system. Because it contains vitamin B12, it has a calming effect on the nervous system. It is usually consumed raw, in salads or with a vinaigrette. Cooked, the young sprouts are delicious with fish.

SCORZONERA HISPANICA **Scorzonera**

Root vegetable
Family: *Compositae*
Origin: *southern and Central Europe*
Height: *8 to 12 inches (20 to 30 cm) (Rosettes)*
Flowering: *spring*
Properties: *tranquilizer, diuretic, nutritious, expectorant, sudorific*

Rhubarb

The plant's fleshy, tart, and highly acid leafstalks are used in pies, often in compotes and preserves, and sometimes as the basis of a wine or an apéritif.

The **scorzonera** grows wild in dry regions and was already known in antiquity for its medicinal properties. It was not cultivated in the garden until the Renaissance, when it became known under the name of black **salsify**. In the 18th century **La Quintinie**, lawyer and agronomist of **King Louis XIV**, described it as a root

with an extraordinary taste. Since then it has become part of European cuisine.

The roots soon replaced that of **salsify**, which was less productive, woody and of lower quality. Today, vegetable lovers prize **scorzonera**. It is a perennial plant with an upright, cylindrical, taproot of approximately 16 inches (40 cm) in length. Its black rind encloses a white, firm, slightly milky flesh that tastes of sweet **almonds**.

The entire, lanceolate leaves are wrapped around the base. The beautiful yellow flowers appear in terminal clusters and bear uniform fruit or achenes which contain a feathery, hairy valve. **Scorzonera** thrives in light, deep soil rich in humus and warm, sunny locations. It is sown directly onto the field in the spring, watering it regularly during the summer. During the first year, the long roots are pulled out, but they can also be left in the soil. If they are harvested after the blooming period of the second year, they will be much larger. This vegetable has a pleasant taste and is very nutritious. It is rich in mucilage, carbohydrates (20%), and latex. It does not have any starch, and it contains inulin which is beneficial for diabetics.

This vegetable is recommended for people suffering from stomach disorders and indigestion. It soothes the intestine and alleviates inflammations. Besides, it is a diuretic and a sudorific, it has a positive effect on the kidneys and the urinary tract; it helps the organism eliminate toxins. It also alleviates irritations in the respiratory system and acts as an expectorant.

Before being consumed, the roots must be peeled and soaked in lemon water so that they do not turn black. They can be prepared raw, cut in pieces and tossed in a salad. They can also be cooked in salted water with a little flour and milk and served as a accompaniment for meat and poultry. They are excellent in fritters and gratins. The young fresh leaves can be used in salads or cooked as a vegetable. In Spain the **scorzonera** is used as an antidote for the poison of a dangerous snake, known as *escorsu*, which is frequently found in Catalonia.

SECHIUM EDULE   *Chayote or Chocho*

Fruit, tuber, shoot and leaf vegetable
Family: *Cucurbitaceae*
Origin: *unknown*
Height: *several feet (climbing liana)*
Flowering: *spring*
Properties: *tranquilizer, diuretic, tonic*

This vegetable plant is known in Réunion as **chocho**, in India as **chochote**, in the Antilles as **christophine** and its tubers as **chinchayotes**. Unknown in the wild, this plant was already being consumed by the native inhabitants of America. It is believed that the Aztecs cultivated it and from there it spread throughout tropical America. Today it is grown predominantly in Costa Rica, the Antilles, Mexico and in the south of France, in Midi and Charente where it prospers very well.

This is a tendril bearing perennial vine with very long stems. Its leaves are alternate, entire, long, ovoid, petioled, angular and lobed with wavy edges. The very tiny white male flowers appear in terminal clusters, while the female ones appear solitarily. They bear elongated fruit, about 6 inches (15 cm) long, which are rippled at the base. Some are green and have a smooth skin, others are yellowish with more or less sharp prickles. These fruit are monosperm; that is, they contain a single seed of the size of an almond. The main root of the plant is strongly branched out with large edible tubers which can weigh about 22 lbs. (10 kg). This plant

is amazing in that it produces edible tubers and fruit. It thrives in rich nourishing soil in warm, protected locations. The fruit are planted in the spring once there is a root and a bud. The young shoots are harvested in the spring, leaving enough behind so that the plant continues to grow. The fruit are harvested from September until early October. The tubers are pulled out just before the first frost.

Chayote contains a lot of water, vitamin B and C, and only a few calories. It is also rich in mineral salts like potassium, iron and magnesium, which are useful to the organism. Because of its water and fiber content, **chayote** promotes the bowel function and stimulates the production of urine. Its tubers, which contain a lot of starch and vitamin C, are a nutritious and easily digestible food.

The fruit are eaten raw, peeled and grated with lemon juice or cut in pieces and cooked with **onions** and curry. They can also be stuffed with meat. The tubers are cooked in water and prepared like **potatoes**. Their starch is used to make cakes and desserts. The young spring shoots are eaten like **asparagus**, and the young leaves like **spinach**.

SOLANUM MELONGENA   *Aubergine, Eggplant*

Fruit vegetable
Family: *Solanaceae*
Origin: *India*
Height: *32 to 36 inches (80 to 90 cm)*
Flowering: *spring*
Properties: *tranquilizer, healing agent, invigorating, laxative, tonic*

Aubergine is native to India, where it has been cultivated since antiquity for its fleshy fruit. It arrived in Spain around the 6th century and it was later found planted in English gardens as an exotic curiosity. **Aubergines** or **eggplants** owe their name to the color and shape of their white variety. In Italy, during the Renaissance, they were considered an extremely poisonous and evil plant known as *Mala insana* (unhealthy apple) because it belongs to the family of the nightshade plants such as belladonna. **Louis XIV** asked **La Quintinie** to grow it in the gardens of Versailles. Nevertheless, it was not until the 19th century that it made its way to our tables.

Aubergine

Aubergines have conquered not only the kitchens of Greece, the Middle East and India, but also those of the entire Mediterranean area. They harmonize particularly well with tomatoes, garlic and olive oil. Just like courgettes, tomatoes, and bell peppers, they are a key ingredient in the classic ratatouille. They are used in vegetable gratins and prepared as fritters. The Greeks use it to prepare moussaka, a meat gratin. It is mashed to a puree to prepare Turkish aubergine caviar which is flavored with lemon and served cold. It is used sautéed as a accompaniment for meat. Aubergine can also be stuffed.

Today's **aubergines** differ in appearance and color from the first that arrived in Europe. This annual plant has an erect, bushy stem, sometimes armed with a few spines; large ovate, slightly lobed leaves; and pendant, violet, characteristically solitary purple flowers. The fruit is a large, egg-shaped berry, varying in color from dark purple to red, yellowish, or sometimes striped with a glossy surface.

The plant needs a warm, protected location and very nutritious soil. In summer it must be watered regularly. Its cultivation is done in plant beds where it is sown from April to May. Once the plant has five leaves, it is replanted. During their growth, they must be regularly trimmed to stimulate the formation of side branches. Four to five months after sowing, the first ripe fruit can be harvested before they become tender and allowing only five to six fruit to mature per plant. Older fruits become bitter. They are quite sensitive and can spoil during transportation.

Aubergines contain a lot of water, few calories and lot of fiber, vitamins B1 and B2, as well as some vitamin C and mineral salts, mainly potassium. Because of the B vitamins they contain, **aubergines** protect the nervous system, promote the renewal of cells, and stimulate the metabolism. Because they have vitamin C, they work as a healing agent for wounds and strengthen the nerves. The potassium in them works as a diuretic, calms the nervous system, stimulates the heart muscles and has a positive effect on the skin.

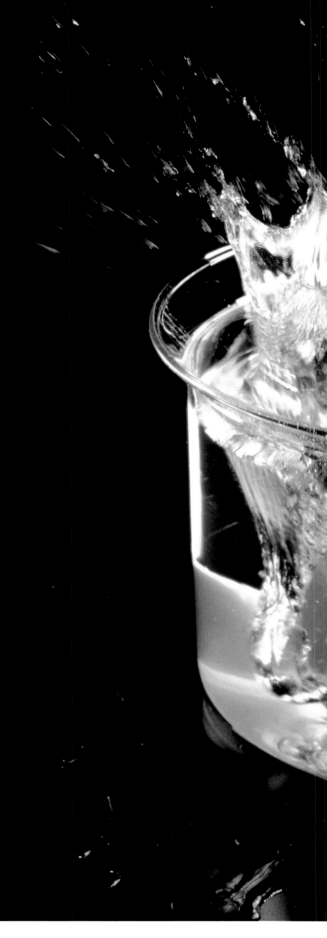

Potatoes

Famous gourmet chefs have dedicated entire books full with original and tasty recipes solely to the potato. Generally it is consumed after being peeled, cooked in water, in oil, in sauces or steamed. They can be prepared in soups, salads, purees, fritters, croquettes, soufflés, gratins, ragouts, fried and even stuffed. Potatoes are marketed whole canned, cooked, fried, and frozen. Potato chips are a common appetizer or snack. The tubers are used to produce a starch which is used to bind sauces and make desserts. Furthermore, a spirit can also be distilled from these tubers.

SOLANUM TUBEROSUM — Potato

Root vegetable
Family: *Solanaceae*
Origin: *South America, the Andes*
Height: *about 20 inches (50 cm)*
Flowering: *spring*
Properties: *soothing, healing agent, diuretic, mineralizing, tonic*

Germany, Poland and Russia are the main **potato** producing countries, while in Britain, **Jersey new potatoes** from the Channel Isles are renowned for their delicate flavor. The **potato** plant is an herbaceous annual with compound leaves consisting of large, oval leaflets with slightly wavy edges. The white or blue flowers have five stamens and a shining yellow pistil. They bear small greenish fruit which contain numerous tiny seeds.

Some **potato** varieties do not bloom and others are sterile. The part of the plant that is harvested are the tubers. There are at least two thousand varieties of **potato**, the **King Edward** variety being one of the most popular in Britain.

The **potato** thrives in light, moist, deep soil, but also tolerates heavier soil that is not too humid. However, it is important to plant it in a sunny location

that is well drained for it does not endure swampy soil or frost. It is cultivated by planting the germinated tubers, from April to May, whole or cut in half at a distance of about 20 inches (50 cm) from each another. When, after about ten days, the shoots appear earth is banked up around the plants. This is repeated as the plants grow. Harvesting takes place, provided there is good weather, two or three months later for early varieties, and five months later for the later ones. Once harvested, the tubers are left to dry in the sun for a day and later are kept in dry, dark storage. If the harvested **potatoes** are exposed to light, their skin tends to turn green. Green **potatoes** are inedible as they contain a poisonous alkaloid known as solanine. **Potatoes** contain 75% of water, vitamins A, B and C. **Potatoes** are a good source of vitamins and energy. They are also rich in starch, carbohydrates (15 to 20 %), proteins (2%) and mineral salts like potassium, which is essential for the body's acid-base balance and muscle function. **Potatoes** are usually recommended during convalescence. Its pulp is a great healing agent for wounds and abscesses. They also help the elimination of toxins from the body. **Potatoes** form one of the most important staple foods of the northern European diet.

SORGHUM BICOLOR   *Sorghum*
Fruit vegetable
Family: Gramineae
Origin: Africa and the Far East
Height: 12 to 20 feet (3.50 to 6 m)
Flowering: spring
Properties: anti-anaemia, invigorating, sedative, stimulant

There are several varieties of **sorghum** raised chiefly for their grain which belong to the species *Sorghum vulgare*. This species includes varieties of **grain sorghums**, **grass sorghums**, and **broomcorn**. **Grain sorghums** include **durra**, **milo**, **shallu**, **kafir corn**, **Egyptian corn**, **great millet**, and **Indian millet**, which is rich in flour.

This strong decorative, annual grass has green, simple leaves with finely dented edges similar to those of **corn**. The leaves are coated with a white waxy substance, and the pith, or central portion, of the stalks is juicy and sweet. The flowers are small, yellow or pink and are grouped in terminal clusters that range from lose to dense. They bear seeds that vary widely among the different types in their color, shape, and size. They have a pleasant, sweet taste, as do the young stems of the plant. **Sorghum** thrives in deep, light and rich soil. It does not like sun, but it is resistant to drought and heat. It is sown at the beginning of spring with regular watering during the first period. It grows quickly; harvesting is done mechanically at the end of the summer.

Sorghum contains plenty of carbohydrates, and starch of which 20 to 30% is amylose and 70 to 80% amylopectin, a rather sweet, jellylike substance. **Sorghum** is also rich in vitamins A, B1, B9, C and E as well as numerous trace elements such as magnesium, zinc, selenium and chrome. **Sorghum** is a healthy, nourishing and digestible cereal. It helps fight against cardio-vascular diseases by reducing the choles-

terol level in the blood. It is a laxative which helps prevent anaemia and fatigue. It also relieves pain caused by inflammations.

Cooked, it is usually used like **rice** as a side dish for meat and fish. The grain is usually ground into a flour to make porridge, unleaven breads, and cakes. The grain is also used in making edible oil, starch, dextrose (a sugar), paste, and alcoholic drinks. The stalks are used as fodder and building materials; the branches are used in the manufacture of paper; and the bark as a natural yellow dye.

SPINACIA OLERACEA   *Spinach*
Leaf vegetable
Family: Chenopodiaceae
Origin: the Middle East, Iran
Height: 8 to 16 inches (20 to 40 cm)
Flowering: summer
Properties: anti-anaemia, healing agent, laxative, mineralizing

---

Spinach was highly prized during the Renaissance thanks to the Medicis who were fond of this green, refreshing leafy vegetable. The preparation of most other leafy vegetables is generally compared to that of **spinach**. Today, this vegetable is very popular in France where it is cultivated in Morbihan, Finistère, Somme, Oise, Aisne, and the North.

Spinach is an annual plant with alternate, lanceolate, thick leaves. They are dark green, fleshy, puckered and slightly wavy on the edges. According to variety, they have a smooth or rough stem. **Spinach** is sometimes monoecious with female and male flowers grouped in clusters on the same plant and a green perianth or floral envelope; or dioecious, having male flowers and female flowers on different plants. They are pollinated by insects and the wind. The flowers bear small seeds with a smooth or prickly husk. **Spinach** requires cool weather and deep, rich, well-limed soil to give quick growth and maximum leaf area. Seed can be sown in rows every two weeks from March to October. The last sowing produce young plants that yield a crop in the autumn and then overwinter, providing leaves in early spring or even throughout the winter if the weather is not too severe.

Spinach contains 90% water, some fiber, and a few calories. However, it is rich in vitamins B1, B2, B9 and C. Furthermore, it contains carotene (vitamin A),

Spinach

Raw spinach is eaten as a salad, by itself or mixed with onions and orange slices. It can also be steamed and served with stock, butter, or cream. Spinach can be served with just about any meat, fish and with hard boiled eggs, fried eggs or omelettes. It can be pureed and used as an ingredient in gratins, soufflés, crepes and, mixed with potato puree, in fritters. Cooked, it is ideal for most forms of pies and quiches, especially when accompanying bacon and onions.

mineral salts (calcium, magnesium zinc and iron), as well as oxalic acid which is responsible for its bitter, sour taste. Because of its oxalate content, **spinach** is not recommended for people suffering from arthritis, rheumatism, gout, kidney and liver ailments, or diabetes. Invigorating, it stimulates vital functions and the digestive system.

It facilitates the elimination of toxins. It is useful to fight against anaemia. **Spinach** facilitates the regeneration of cells and stimulates growth in children. The green water resulting for cooking **spinach** is useful as a coloring agent for food or to color hard boiled eggs for Easter.

STACHYS AFFINIS　　　**Chinese artichoke**
Root vegetable
Family: Labiatae
Origin: Asia
Height: 16 inches (40 cm)
Flowering: rarely in temperate areas
Properties: antispasmodic, laxative, digestive, mineralizing, tonic

---

This is a hardy plant with underground creeping shoots on which small, white tubers form. Its thin, hairy, aerial stem has opposite, long, oval green leaves with crimped edges and visible veins. The small flowers are pink and are borne on terminal clusters.

In temperate climate zones, the **Chinese artichoke** hardly ever blooms and only rarely bears seeds. The tubers, which are the edible part of the plant, have a white flesh and a beige rind. Measuring between 1 and 2 inches (3 and 5 cm) long, the tubers have a knobby shape and are grouped in rings. Their taste resembles that of **artichokes** or **salsify**.

The **Chinese artichoke** needs a sunny location with light, sandy, dry, airy soil. In order to propagate it, the tubers are buried at the beginning of the spring in groups of three or four. The first harvest can take place about eight months later once the shoots have withered. Once they have been dug up, the vegetables become soft very quickly; so they are left in the earth during the entire winter, and are only harvesting according to demand.

The tubers owe their taste to the essential oils which they contain. They are rich in carbohydrates, starch, lipids and cellulose. They contain few vitamins,

Chinese artichoke
Before preparing this vegetable it must be thoroughly rubbed with a cloth and washed in running water to remove the soil. The tubers can be eaten raw in a salad. Briefly cooked, so as not to become soft, they are served with melted butter, or stock. They can also be sautéed with parsley and garlic or prepared as sweet-and-sour fritters or as a gratin with béchamel sauce.

but many minerals. As they contain few calories, they often form part of weight loss diets. They stimulate bile activity, and are recommended to fight bile and liver ailments. Moreover, they have an antispasmodic and slightly hypotensive effect.

TRAGOPOGON PORRIFOLIUS　　　**Salsify or Oyster plant**
Root vegetable
Family: Compositae
Origin: Central Europe
Height: 8 to 12 inches (20 to 30 cm)
Flowering: spring (from the second year)
Properties: purifier, diuretic, invigorating, sudorific

Salsify was already very popular among the Romans, even serving as a motive for frescoes in Pompeii. **Apicius**, the famous Roman gourmet, had several recipes dedicated to this vegetable. In the 17th century, **Olivier de Serres**, a minister of **Henry IV**, referred to it as "sersifi". However, in those times, the **Spanish scorzonera** was preferred. Today it is sold only canned; it is unavailable fresh. Nevertheless, it has become popular among some private market gardeners who grow these tasty and delicate roots in their gardens.

Salsify is a biennial herb with a thick white taproot. It bares narrow, often keeled leaves whose basis usually clasp the stem forming a tuft at the base of the plant. Together with the root they are the edible parts of the plant. The blue-purple flowers are borne in clusters on long peduncles. They bear fruit with a feathery panache forming a fluffy ball similar to that of a dandelion. The long, fleshy, fusiform taproot has a white-yellow rind.

Salsify thrives in a sunny location with light, deep, moist soil rich in nutrients. It is grown from seed in spring directly onto the field. During the whole summer, the soil must be kept moist by regular watering. The harvesting of the leaves and roots is done from October to March, before the plant blooms.

Salsify contains many carbohydrates (12%), proteins and cellulose. It has a considerably high nutritional value. It also has a white latex resin which becomes red when it comes in contact with the air. **Salsify** is also a source of vitamins A and C. It is a nutritious vegetable which helps the body eliminate impuri-

ties and toxins from the blood. Moreover, it has a diuretic and sudorific effect; thereby promoting the elimination of uric acid. Aside from its nutritional properties, this vegetable is helpful in the decontamination, purification and regeneration of body organs. The fleshy buds are harvested in the spring and are consumed raw with fruit and other vegetables.

Salsify leaves, which have a taste similar to that of chicory, are also used in salads, while the roots have a nutty taste and are consumed cooked alone or sprinkled with butter, meat juices or a béchamel sauce. They are sautéed with parsley and mixed with other vegetables, or used in omelettes, fritters or stews. Salsify goes well with white meat. Its cooking water is a refreshing, fragrant drink.

TRICHOSANTHES ANGUINA   *Snake gourd*
Fruit vegetable
Family: Cucurbitaceae
Origin: South-East Asia, India, Sri Lanka
Height: about 13 feet (4 m)
Flowering: spring
Properties: soothing, purifier, diuretic, stimulant

The snake gourd is a fast growing vine which, long before being cultivated, was consumed by the inhabitants of the regions where it grew wild. Today it is a rather popular vegetable used in several traditional recipes. They are generally easy to find in Asian grocery shops when in season.

It is an annual climber with more or less palmate, two or three lobed leaves with a long petiole. It has entire, notched or slightly wavy leaflets with serrated edges. Its flowers have long fringes on the petals, and while male flowers are borne in clusters, female flowers are solitary. They bear edible, oddly shaped fruit that look like coiled up snakes. They are plain green or grey-green becoming orange or red when ripe. Their rind is thin and the flesh thick and juicy. Like cucumbers, they contain numerous small, flat, ovoid, and tender seeds which, when the fruit is ripe, become big and hard. They have a delicate, sweet taste.

Snake gourd needs a rich, moist, well drained soil with a sunny and warm exposure. It is sown directly onto the field in the spring with a support to facilitate climbing. During the growth period, they must be watered regularly. Approximately eight weeks after sowing, the first fruits, which are tender, juicy and well developed, can be harvested.

Snake gourd contains a lot of water and fiber, but only a few calories. It is rich in proteins, vitamins A, B and C as well as minerals (manganese, potassium, iron and iodine). It is a diuretic that helps the organism by eliminating its impurities. It has a relaxing effect on the bodily tissue; thereby, soothing inflammations. It also has a positive and soothing effect on the nervous system. It stimulates blood circulation and contributes to cleansing the blood of toxins.

Just like green beans, snake gourd is cut into pieces and cooked in boiling salted water for five to ten minutes. It can be served with a curry sauce, salads, vegetable soups, ragouts, or couscous. It can also be added to other vegetables, cooked with tomatoes and onions, or mixed with minced meat or chopped fish. The young shoots and leaves are also eaten in salads or stews.

TRITICUM AESTIVUM   *Wheat*
Fruit vegetable
Family: Gramineae
Origin: the Middle East, Ethiopia
Height: 36 to 48 inches (90 to 120 cm)
Flowering: spring
Properties: anti-anaemia, reduces cholesterol, invigorating, purifier, emollient, laxative, mineralizing, stimulant

---

Wheat is probably the offspring of a species originating in Abyssinia, when a single large, hard seed accidentally crossed with an unknown cereal, producing a species with multiple grains which was farther improved over the course of time by selection. To date, there have been approximately 12,000 varieties documented. From the Middle Eastern agricultural societies it spread to Egypt where it is widely grown today. Wheat is the most important grain of the northern hemisphere. In Africa it is also grown on a wide scale, especially in South Africa and the Maghreb countries.

Wheat, as we know it today, is an annual, herbaceous plant with flat, branching roots. The wheat plant has a long, thin, hollow aerial stem with nodes. The leaves are long, slender, straight and pointed wrapped around the stem at the base forming a sheath.

Wheat
Whole wheat is a grain similar to rice. It must be soaked in cold water overnight and then cooked in salted water. It can also be cooked pilaf-style: that is, sautéed in oil, covered with water and boiled. Wheat semolina is an indispensable ingredient for couscous. Cooked in milk it is used to make vanilla or caramel cakes with raisins or other dried fruit. Wheat flour is used in making cakes, bread, desserts, pasta, ravioli, and bread crumbs, as well as to bind sauces. Dried, wheat is popular as a breakfast cereal.

The flowers are grouped together in spikelets, each having two to six flowers. They bear dry fruit or monocotyledon caryopsis, which contain in each case a separate kernel.

Though grown under a wide range of climates and soils, **wheat** is best adapted to temperate regions with moderate rainfall. In general, **wheat** requires loose, fertilized, well drained soil.

Winter and spring **wheat** are the two major types of crop, with the severity of the winter expected determining whether a winter or spring type is cultivated. Winter **wheat** is always sown in the autumn; spring **wheat** is generally sown in the spring but can be sown in the autumn where winters are mild. Seeds germinate rather quickly covering the fields in winter with fresh green shoots. Spring rain promotes their growth. In July, when they are yellow and the seeds are swollen, the plant is harvested mechanically.

On average, the kernel contains 12% water, 70% of carbohydrates, 12% proteins, 2% fat, 2.2% crude fibers, 1.8% minerals (potassium, phosphorus and calcium), as well as vitamins of the B group and vitamin C. Moreover, the germ is a source of lecithin and phosphorus. The composition of the **wheat** grain is, therefore, a major source of energy in the human diet.

The lecithin it contains helps lower cholesterol levels and has a preventive effect against arteriosclerosis and cardio-vascular diseases. Vitamin E is a natural antioxidant that fights against the accumulation of toxins in the body. Phosphorus promotes the formation of bones and teeth. Potassium and calcium nourish the nervous system, regulate the activity of the heart muscle, and improve skin condition. B vitamins stimulate the activity of the stomach, transform sugar in the body, and promote formation of red blood cells. **Wheat** lowers the risk of rickets. **Wheat** is also used to calm inflammations, sooth body tissue and increase vital functions.

In all its forms and varieties, **wheat** is the most popular and most complete cereal there is. Although most **wheat** is grown for human food, small quantities are used by industry for the production of starch, paste, malt, dextrose, gluten, alcohol, and other products.

In some regions **wheat** straw is used to thatch roofs. In Tuscany it is used to manufacture excellent straw hats which are to be preferred to imitations made from synthetic materials.

Stinging nettle
Its leaves, which are previously washed and quickly blanched to remove the stinging barbs, are used in potato salads, stuffings, egg dishes, omelettes, minced meat, pâtés and as a garnish for savory pies. Steamed, they are used like spinach. Stinging nettle soup is made in the following way: first fry bacon rashers in a pan until brown. Sprinkle them with flour and mix to a roux. Add a quarter of a liter of stock, stirring vigorously to prevent lumps forming and bring to the boil. Add the finely chopped stinging nettle leaves and let simmer for ten minutes. Add a further cup of stock, heavy cream, and season with salt and pepper. Serve warm with grated cheese on top.

URTICA DIOICA ET URENS   **Nettle and Stinging nettle**

Leaf vegetable
Family: Urticaceae
Origin: worldwide, except in South America and equatorial Africa
Height: about 2 to 5 feet (0.50 to 1.50 m)
Flowering: June to October
Properties: anti-anaemia, anti-diabetes, astringent, laxative, diuretic, emetic

---

Nettle is a hardy plant which is able to colonize large areas within a short time by growing abundant underground rhizomes which produce the sharply edged stems covered with fine hairs, and which branch out when cut back. The opposite, elliptical leaves have dented borders and are also covered with hairs.

Inflorescences are borne on leaf axiles and are formed by long, hanging female flowers and shorter, upright male flowers which bear numerous seeds.

Stinging nettle is an annual plant of smaller size. It has a fusiform, simple root and smaller, opposite leaves with elliptical stalks and dented edges. The male flowers, which are more numerous than female flowers, are borne in clusters and bear several seeds which can continue to germinate for a number of years.

Stinging nettle has an astringent, bitter taste. Even though it prefers soil that is rich in nitrates and phosphates, it generally adapts itself to almost all conditions. **Stinging nettle** is sown in late winter, while **nettle** is propagated by rhizome division in the autumn. **Stinging nettle** leaves are harvested as a vegetable and herbal seasoning from the beginning of spring until the end of autumn. The young **nettle** shoots are harvested from April to May; the crown of the plant and the tender leaves are harvested later.

Stinging nettle contains a lot of nitrogen, chlorophyll, proteins, fat, carbohydrates, minerals (calcium, iron, silicon and zinc), organic acids, tannin, flavonoides, vitamins A, B2 and B5, as well as a lot of vitamin C. All these contents stimulate bodily functions, promote the formation of blood, work against inflammations, chronic cystitis and diabetes, and alleviate rheumatic pain.

The high levels of chlorophyll, cellulose, vitamin C, and glycogen lower the level of sugar in the blood. Moreover, the dried leaves contain 20% proteins and approximately 2% fat.

Because of its components, **nettle** is used to prevent broken nails and hair loss. Due to the fact that it contains zinc, it is also used to treat acne. It has a mineralizing effect on cartilage and relives arthritis and rheumatism. Furthermore, it is used to fight against fatigue, stimulate the gall bladder, and improve digestion.

VALERIANELLA OLITORIA **Corn salad, Lamb's lettuce**

Leaf vegetable
Family: *Valerianaceae*
Origin: *Sardinia, Sicily*
Height: *about 4 inches (10 cm)*
Flowering: *spring*
Properties: *soothing, tranquilizer, purifier, laxative*

Corn salad or **lamb's lettuce** is a vegetable that has been used as a salad since antiquity. It previously grew wild and was collected by the rural population from meadows and from between the rows of vines in vineyards.

Corn salad is a herbaceous, annual plant with elongated, characteristically veined leaves grouped in basal rosettes. The hollow stems are branched out in the shape of a fork and can reach a height of 8 to 12 inches (20 to 30 cm). The small, white or bluish umbel flowers are borne in terminal clusters. The leaves have a fresh, sticky, nutty taste.

There are more than 50 species. **Corn salad** grows best in damp, relatively hard soil in the shade. It is sown in mid-summer to be harvested in the autumn, at the end of the summer to be harvested in winter, or at the end of September to be harvested in the spring. **Corn salad** is resistant to cold. Harvesting is done once the leaf rosettes are well formed before blooming while they still have not acquired a bitter taste.

Corn salad has a higher nutritional value than that of other lettuces. It is rich in vitamins A, B and C, minerals (iron, phosphorus and calcium) as well as saccharides, proteins, and fat.

Corn salad stimulates digestion and has a soothing effect on the nervous system.

It is eaten raw by itself or mixed with other vegetables in a salad. It goes well with green salads, **beetroot** or **potatoes**. It can also be used to make herbal soups, omelettes and pâtés.

VICIA FABA **Broad or Fava bean**

Fruit vegetable
Family: *Papilionaceae*
Origin: *the Middle East*
Height: *about 3 feet (1 m)*
Flowering: *spring*
Properties: *antispasmodic, diuretic, purifier, sedative*

Broad bean is a perennial legume. It has erect stems and branches crowded with compound leaves with four leaflets. The flowers are borne on terminal clusters with a large white corolla that is stained black. They bear long, green, rough pods which become brown when ripe. The pods contain large, irregularly flattened seeds. The plant is not very demanding, but it grows best in moist, limey soil rich in humus with a warm, sunny exposure. It is sown in February or March in rows with three to four seeds per seeding place. In very mild regions, it can be sown from October to February. Harvesting is generally done while the **broad bean** is still green; **broad beans**, raw or cooked, are consumed when young.

Young **broad beans** have a low nutritional value. However, they are rich in proteins (23%), magnesium, vitamin C and fiber. The plant is a diuretic and its high content of fiber facilitates digestion and helps fight intestinal spasms. The dried **beans** are rich in minerals and carbohydrates (55%). Because they contain more calories, they are more nutritious than the green beans. **Broad beans** are known to soothe pain and slow the activity of the nervous system.

XANTHOSOMA SAGITTIFOLIUM **Tania, Yautia**

Root and leaf vegetable
Family: *Araceae*
Origin: *tropical America*
Height: *about 6.5 feet (2 m)*
Flowering: *spring*
Properties: *emollient, nutritious, mineralizing*

Also known as **yautia** or **okumo** in Venezuela, the **tania** is a staple food in Central and South America. It contains calcium oxalate which is a highly toxic substance that is difficult to dissolve. The corns must, therefore, be thoroughly washed and cooked

Broad bean

Broad beans can be eaten raw with salt, pickled in oil or in salads. When they are fresh, they can be cooked and served as a side dish for meat and other vegetables. They can be sautéed in butter with scallions and served with pork or sausages. When dried they must first be soaked overnight before being cooked. They are then boiled in order to remove their coarse husks. They can be cooked to a puree, in a gratin or in a ragout. Fava bean flour mixed with wheat flour is used to prepare biscuits and cakes to which it adds a nutty flavor.

Corn

Sweet corn can be eaten whole, raw or cooked in water, milk or steamed. It is a traditional accompaniment for grilled meat and fowl as well as for pork or lamb patties. The delicate kernels are the basic ingredient in many salads, meat and fish recipes. They can be used in stuffings and vegetable mixtures. Corn flour is used to make porridge, puddings, cakes, polenta, and biscuits. Mixed with wheat flour it is used to make a very heavy bread. Popcorn is obtained from a variety that has very small kernels; heated in oil, the kernels explode becoming puffy and soft. They are usually eaten salted or sweet. In Mexico fermented corn is used to make an alcoholic drink known as "chicha." When the young spikes are approximately 4 inches (10 cm) they are cut, pickled in vinegar and served as a savory snack. The can also be cooked in salted water like a vegetable and used in salads or served with exotic dishes. Corn semolina is an ingredient for cornflakes. Starch is also obtained from corn. It is used to bind sauces, and to prepare soups, fine pastries and milk puddings.

before they are edible. Today the plant is cultivated worldwide.

Tania has tuberous rhizomes and very large, abundant, leaves with long petioles. Its stems, which can be over 3 feet (1 m) long, are triangular, in the form of an arrow or oval with a glossy topside and a lustrous underside. Flowers and fruit rarely develop. **Tania** requires a warm climate and damp, nourishing, deep soil. It is cultivated by replanting the tubers in the autumn. The harvesting of the shoots and young leaves takes place in the spring; the tubers are harvested at the end of the summer. Because the entire plant contains calcium oxalate, caution must be taken. Once the tubers are pulled out, they are left to dry in the sun for a day and placed in cool, dry and dark storage.

Tania contains a lot of starch, carbohydrates, amino acids, minerals (potassium and calcium), vitamins A and B as well as different fibers. The tubers stimulate digestion, alleviate inflammations, and prevent the absorption of fat and sugar in the intestine. They mineralize cartilage and strengthen the organism.

Once the calcium oxalate has been washed out, the tubers are cooked in water, steamed or fried. Peeled and mashed they make a delicious puree. Cut in pieces and cooked in the pressure cooker with herbs, they are used as an accompaniment for meat and fish. They go well in a ragout served with poultry. The starch of the tubers is used to prepare porridges, noodles, creams and cakes. The young flowers and the shoots are eaten cooked as green vegetables.

ZEA MAYS   **Corn**
Fruit vegetable
Family: *Gramineae*
Origin: *Mexico, origin of the wild form unknown*
Height: *about 8 feet (2.50 m)*
Flowering: *spring*
Properties: *tranquilizer, analgesic, anti-cholesterol, diuretic*

The tall, annual grass has a stout, erect, solid stem and large narrow leaves. Staminate or male flowers are borne on the tassel terminating the main axis of the stem, while the female flower is borne on the leaf axiles. Female flowers, which mature to become the ear, are spikes with a thickened axis, bearing paired spikelets normally producing seeds through self-pollination.

In the case of selected **corn** varieties kernels stand all around a woody central spike that is enclosed by modified leaves or husks. The leaves are large, lanceolate and narrow with wavy margins, spaced alternately on opposite sides of the stem. The roots are not anchored particularly deep in the soil.

Corn needs nourishing, deep, loose, moist soil with a sunny exposure. It is sown in rows from May to June once the earth has been warmed by the Sun. So that the plants grow strong, they must be frequently banked with earth. Regular and extensive watering is necessary. Harvesting is done according to the variety concerned. **Sweet corn** (*Zea mays var. saccharata*) which is consumed like a fresh vegetable, is harvested once the kernels are well formed, but still tender and juicy. **Cereal corn** is harvested mechanically early in the autumn when the shoots begin to wilt and the kernels are ripe.

Sweet corn is rich in carbohydrates, vitamin A, vitamins of the B group and vitamin C. Besides, it contains minerals, particularly magnesium, phosphorus and potassium. It is high in calories. **Cereal corn** contains 75% starch, 5% sugar, 7–9% lipids, and minerals. It is a very nourishing grain, but less balanced than **wheat**. Although it slows down the activity of the thyroid and regulates the metabolism, **corn** as basic food cannot replace **wheat** for it has an inferior nutritional value.

The germ contains, like that of sunflowers, an oil which reduces the levels of cholesterol. Its starch is easy to digest, especially for people with delicate and weak stomachs. Its spikelets contain salisylic acid, which has an analgesic and anti-inflammatory effect, and vitamin K, which is indispensable for blood clotting. It is both diuretic and soothing.

Corn leaves are used as livestock feed and the grains are used to feed fowl and swine. The stalks are made into paper and wallboard, while the cobs are used for fuel and in the preparation of industrial solvents.

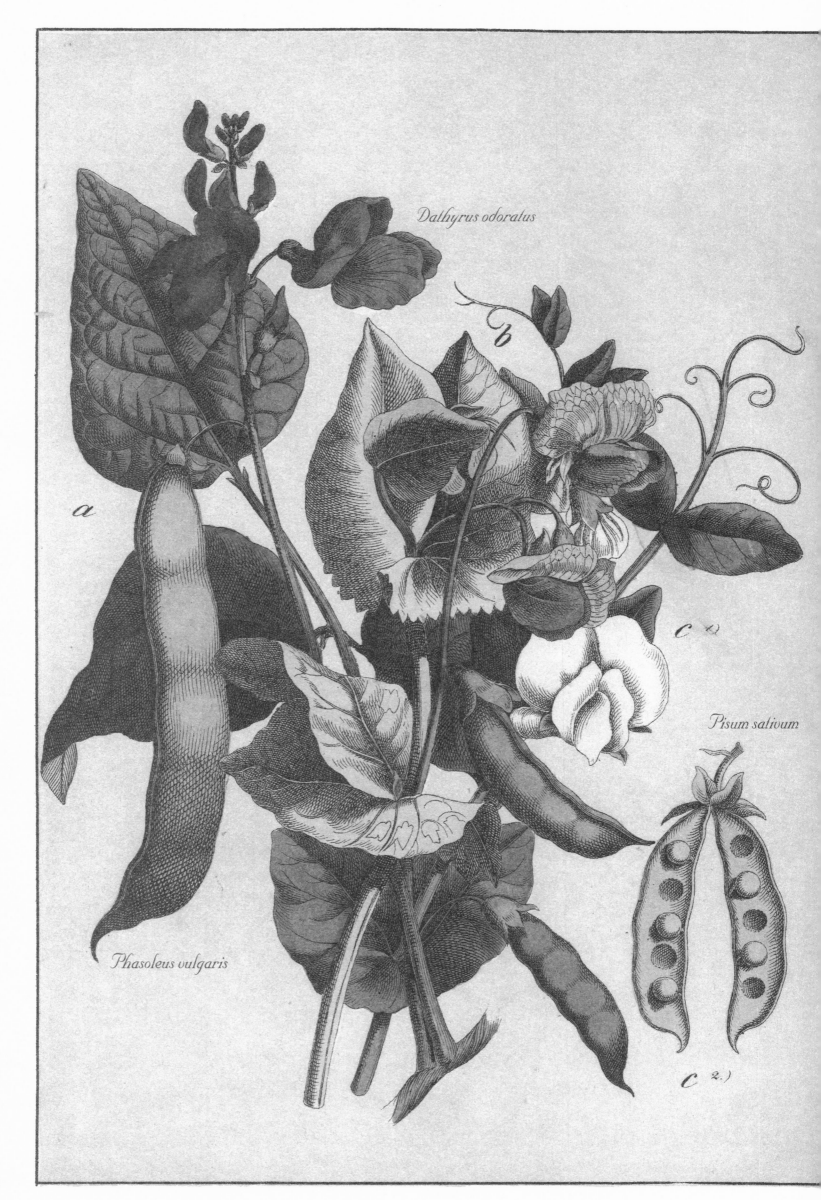

Dathyrus odoratus

b

c

Pisum sativum

a

Phasoleus vulgaris

C 2.)

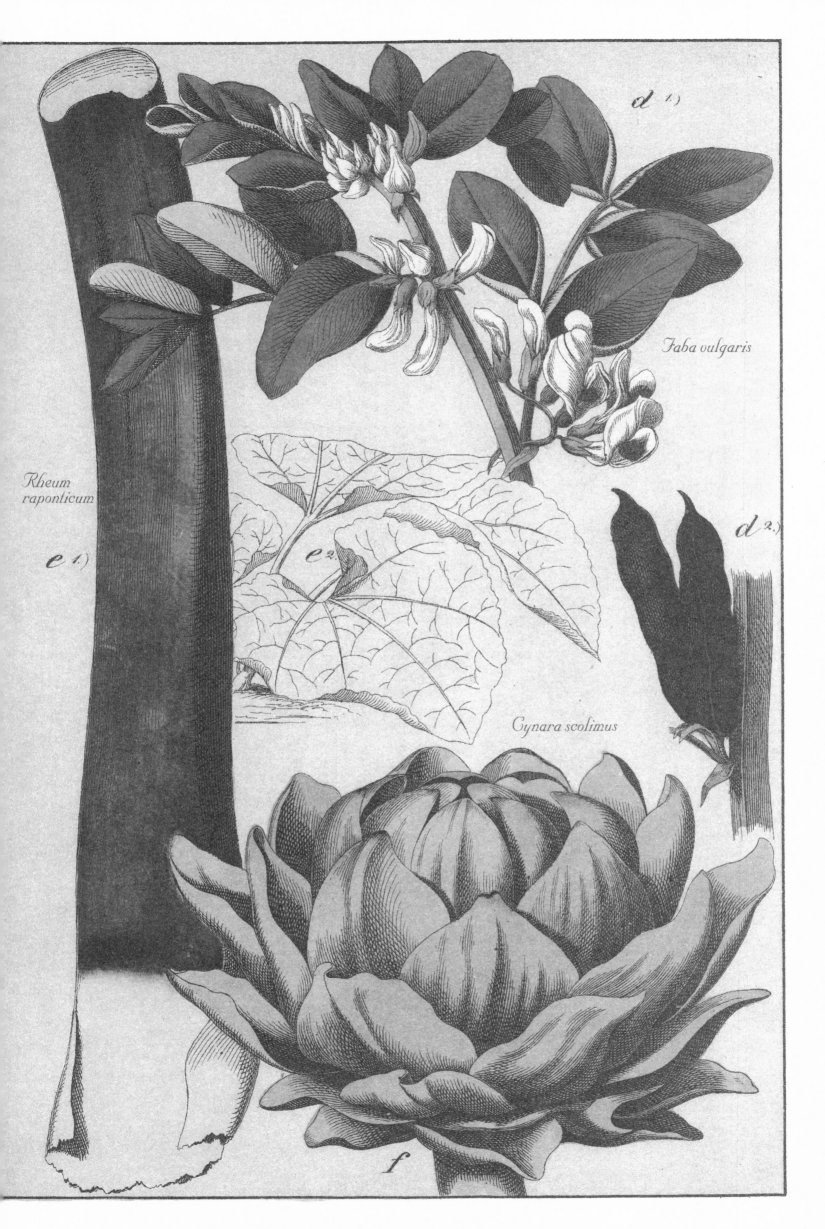

Faba vulgaris

Rheum raponticum

d 1)

d 2)

e 1)

e 2.

Cynara scolimus

f

123

a 1)

a 3)

a 2)

Raphanus sativus

Apium graveslens

c

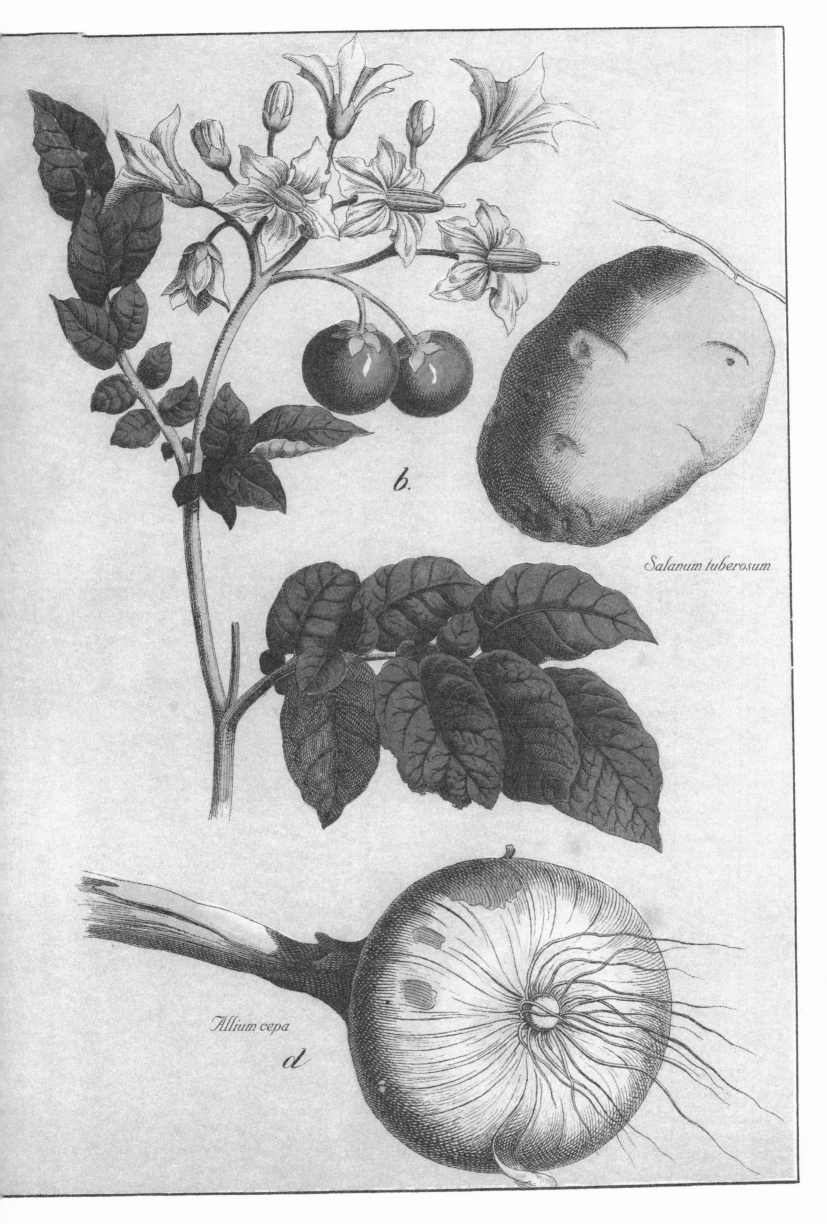

b.

Salanum tuberosum

Allium cepa

d

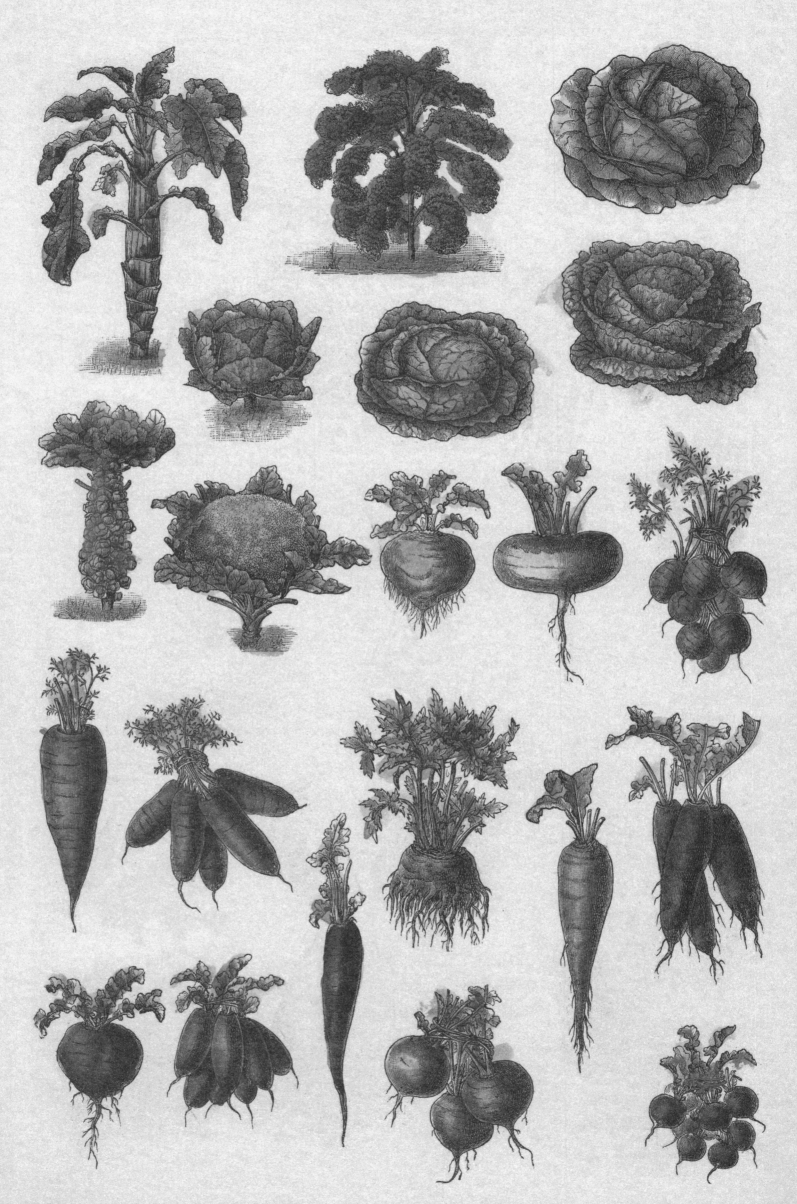

INDEX OF LATIN NAMES

AND OF ENGLISH NAMES

BIBLIOGRAPHY

Berry, Susan: Kitchen Harvest: A Cook's Guide to Growing Organic Fruits,
Vegetables, and Herbs, 2002

Brown, Lynda: Gardeners' World Vegetables for Small Gardens, 1994

Chandler, Lynda E.: Fruits and Vegetables, 2001

Heaton, Donald D.: A Produce Reference Guide to Fruits and Vegetables
from Around the World – Nature's Harvest, 1997

Katz, Pat: Parsley, Peppers, Potatoes & Peas: A Cook's Companion for Handling,
Using & Storing a Garden's Bounty, 2002

King, Darlene: Vegetables You Used to Hate!, 2000

Patenaude, Fredric: Sunfood Cuisine: A Practical Guide to Raw Vegetarian Cuisine, 2002

Robinson, Fay: Vegetables, Vegetables (Rookie Read-About Science), 1994

Robinson, Kathleen / Luckett, Pete: Vegetarian's A to Z Guide to Fruits & Vegetables, 1996

Shewfelt, Robert L.: Fruit and Vegetable Quality: An Integrated View, 2000

Smit, Tim / Macmillan Browse, Philip: The Heligan Vegetable Bible, 2000

Van Den Berg, Oona: The Exotic Fruit and Vegetable Handbook, 2001